Rare Plants of S ....ne

3rd edition

Alexander J. Lockton & Sarah J. Whild

with illustrations by Sarah Whild

Shropshire Botanical Society

2005

Published by the
Shropshire Botanical Society
Preston Montford Field Centre
Montford Bridge
Shropshire
SY4 2DX

2005

ISBN 0 9530937 1 9

First published by Shrewsbury Museum Service, 1995 (ISBN 0 9500122 7 0)

Second edition published by the Shropshire Flora Group, 1997 (ISBN 0 9530937 0 0)

Text & maps © Alex Lockton & Sarah Whild 2005

Illustrations © Sarah Whild 2005

Maps were produced using DMap for Windows, supplied by Dr Alan Morton. Map outlines and grid references are based on the Ordnance Survey maps and reproduced under Licence No. 100040428.

Data storage and analysis was performed using Recorder 3.4, supplied by the Joint Nature Conservation Committee.

The Shropshire Botanical Society (www.shropshirebotany.org.uk) is an independent association of professionals and amateurs concerned with botany, ecology and conservation in Shropshire.

Printed by Livesey Ltd., Shrewsbury (01743) 235651

Contents

Introduction

The Botanical Society of the British Isles has, in recent years, encouraged the production of County Rare Plant Registers to complement the more traditional botanical publications. Some are little more than lists of six-figure grid references given in confidential reports, while others, such as Rare Plants of Shetland (Scott *et al.* 2002), are beautifully illustrated books on sale to the public. In essence, they are the edited highlights of a full county Flora and, as such, they are much quicker and cheaper to produce. Following in the tradition of the Ecological Flora of the Shropshire Region (Sinker *et al.* 1985), Rare Plants of Shropshire is intended primarily for ecologists, so it contains historical records and NVC communities rather than colour photographs and detailed grid references.

This third edition incorporates many new (and additional historical) records and gives more analysis, with the intention of providing better and updated information to nature conservationists and ecologists. We have tried our best to give an accurate representation of the facts and to consider the implications of changes in the flora. We have also attempted to give a realistic perspective of rare plants – when they are important to an issue and when they are not.

A significant change since our second edition has been the categorisation of plants into three statuses: native, archaeophyte and neophyte (Preston & Pearman 2004, Preston, Pearman & Hall 2004). We have adapted the process to make it applicable at the county level, without being too strict about dates of first records. It is a useful system for describing the origins and ecological niches of the various species, but its should not be taken too far. Native does not mean 'good' and the other categories do not equate to 'bad.'

Native plants are those which are believed to have arrived in the county independently of human activity, and which tend to occur in natural habitat types such as woodland and lakes. Archaeophytes are those which were brought here by people, deliberately or inadvertently, during the last few thousand years and which have become established in semi-natural habitats such as hay meadows and arable fields. Neophytes are recent introductions, usually as garden escapes or in response to modern activities such as spreading salt on roads in winter.

This report is primarily about native species, but some archaeophytes and neophytes are covered if they are of interest. The BSBI's guidelines (Farrell & Perring 1996, Lockton, Whild & Pearman 2001) for inclusion in a county rare plant register are given below.

Criteria for inclusion
1. Endemic species (those that occur only in the British Isles).

2. Internationally rare species cited in the Bern Convention, IUCN lists or the European Habitats Directive.

3. Nationally Rare species that occur in 15 or fewer 10km squares (hectads) in Britain.

4. Nationally Scarce species that occur in 16-100 hectads in Britain.

5. Locally Rare species that occur in three or fewer sites in the county.

6. Locally Scarce species that occur in ten or fewer sites in the county and which are thought to be declining.

Critical taxa and hybrids are covered to varying degrees, and full details are given where known, but there are undoubtedly many omissions. We can only apologise for these and hope to gather better information in future.

The current report is based on 4,921 records of 238 taxa (including species, subspecies, varieties and hybrids).

In the Endemic category, there is just one species that may be endemic to Shropshire, *Fumaria painteri*, but its taxonomic status is somewhat uncertain, and it has not been seen for nearly a hundred years. The only species currently found in the county that is endemic to the British Isles is English Whitebeam *Sorbus anglica*.

In the second category, Internationally Rare, there are two species. Floating Water-plantain *Luronium natans* is restricted to western Europe and is apparently declining throughout its range. It is protected under the Bern Convention and the EC Habitats Directive and under the Wildlife & Countryside Act. Purple Ramping-fumitory *Fumaria purpurea* is almost endemic to the British Isles, but has been recorded several times in the Channel Isles.

Apart from the English Whitebeam, we have just one plant that is considered to be Nationally Rare (i.e. present in fewer than 16 hectads in Britain). This is Scarce Prickly-sedge *Carex muricata* ssp. *muricata*. It is currently considered to be Critically Endangered (Wigginton 1999), which means (in essence) having fewer than 250 plants in the wild plus a serious decline in the last ten years. As there are at least 1,000 plants in Shropshire alone, and no evidence of decline, its status should probably be downgraded to 'Endangered', but it is still a very rare plant. It is common and widespread on the Continent, however, and there are some uncertainties about its taxonomic status.

There are twenty species (including *F. purpurea*) in the Nationally Scarce category that are currently found in Shropshire. Some are quite widespread, and are specialities of the county, while others are on the brink of extinction. The list is given below.

Nationally Scarce plants
Aconitum napellus, Monk's-hood
Bromopsis benekenii, Lesser Hairy-brome
Campanula patula, Spreading Bell-flower
Carex digitata, Fingered Sedge
C. elongata, Elongated Sedge
C. montana, Soft-leaved Sedge
Cicuta virosa, Cowbane
Dianthus deltoides, Maiden Pink
Epipactis phyllanthes, Green-flowered Helleborine
Galeopsis angustifolia, Red Hemp-nettle
Gentiana pneumonanthe, Marsh Gentian
Helleborus foetidus, Stinking Hellebore
Hordelymus europaeus, Wood Barley

Impatiens noli-tangere, Touch-me-not Balsam
Nuphar pumila, Least Water-lily
Orobanche rapum-genistae, Greater Broomrape
Sedum forsterianum, Rock Stonecrop
Thelypteris palustris, Marsh Fern
Tilia platyphyllos, Large-leaved Lime

Some 99 taxa have here been classified as locally rare, and 43 are locally scarce. Which species to include as scarce is very much a matter of opinion, and it might have been possible to list more. Perhaps more can be added in future editions.

Acknowledgements
A large number of people have contributed information that has been used in this report. They are all acknowledged in the list of recorders and determiners, and in the individual species accounts, but we would also like to express our gratitude to them for contributing their records and making reports such as this possible.

Roger Green has been invaluable for organising the printing and finances of this publication.

David Pearman and Guy & Mavis Lockton kindly proof-read the drafts.

John Bingham, Kate Thorne and Ruth Dawes all gave their time resurveying old sites on request.

Jonathan Briggs, Mark Hill, Owen Mountford, David Pearman, Chris Preston and Chris Walker provided information on past records and recorders.

The Botanical Society would like to thank Sue Townsend and the Field Studies Council for hosting our meetings and providing a base, as well as supporting and encouraging natural history in the county for many years.

The Botanical Society of the British Isles (www.bsbi.org.uk) organises and coordinates botanical recording in Britain & Ireland. Without their publications, referees and support to county recorders, this report would not have been possible. David McCosh and Tim Rich have been particularly helpful with hawkweeds and fumitories respectively.

Map of Shropshire

The area covered by this report is vice county 40, which is roughly (but not exactly) the same as the modern county of Shropshire and the Borough of Telford & Wrekin. It occurs entirely within the 100km squares SJ and SO of the Ordnance Survey national grid. The area of the county is 3,464 km^2, making it the tenth largest of the 113 vice counties in Britain. It has a population of 442,000 people, giving one of the lowest population densities in England. The main towns and rivers are shown on the map below.

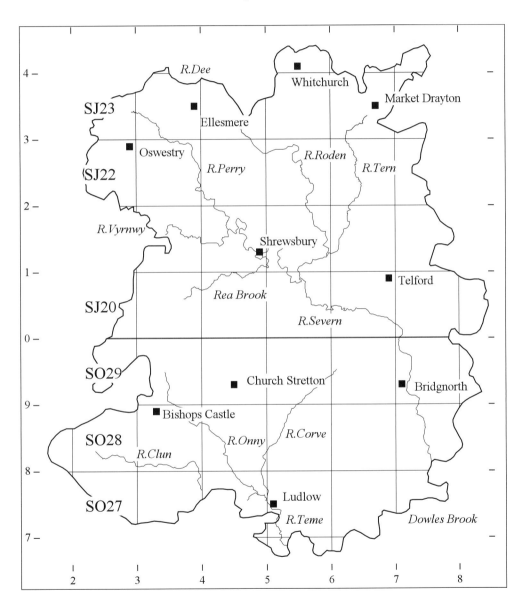

Recorders

Our knowledge of the flora of Shropshire is the result of nearly four centuries of work by the county's botanists, recording species, collecting specimens and taking visiting experts to see interesting places. The first rare plant records from the county were made in 1632, when George Bowles (1604-1672) visited William Coote (1590-1640) at Chirbury and they found 'Codded Arsmart' *Impatiens noli-tangere* at Marrington Dingle and Great Sundew *Drosera anglica* in the extensive bogs south of The Mere, Ellesmere (Oswald 1985, 1995). Both were additions to the British list.

Edward Lhwyd (1660-1709) was the first Salopian botanist of note, although he did not record any rare plants in the county, except the ones he planted on his father's estate at Llanforda. Littleton Brown (1699-1749) was a friend of Johann Dillenius (1684-1747) and Samuel Brewer (1670-1743), and he took them to see several interesting species during their brief stop in Shropshire on the way to Wales in 1726.

Several names stand out as particularly significant. Edward Williams (1762-1833) was one of the great botanists of his generation, although he published very little and is almost unknown outside the county. He was the first to find Six-stamened Waterwort *Elatine hexandra* and Red Pondweed *Potamogeton alpinus* in Britain. He also collected the type specimen of the hybrid sedge *Carex* ×*fulva*. His unpublished manuscript, which may have been written in about 1800, was discovered by William Leighton (1805-1889) in 1841, just as his own Flora was going to print. Leighton managed to insert most of Williams's records either into the body of the text or into his extensive 'additions and corrections' section. Leighton's transcription of Williams's manuscript is still available to view at Shrewsbury library.

The proof of the quality and quantity of Williams's records is that even now he ranks as the most prolific recorder of rare plants in the county, if you discount those of us who have made it our business to seek them out over the last few years.

The top 20 rare plant recorders

		No. of records	…species
1.	S.J. Whild	433	103
2.	A.J. Lockton	400	95
3.	E. Williams	242	94
4.	W.E. Beckwith	232	94
5.	C. Walker	187	56
6.	W.A. Leighton	150	75
7.	W. Phillips	138	85
8.	C.A. Sinker	139	71
9.	J. Bingham	149	31
10.	A.K. Thorne	107	44
11.	R.M. Stokes	77	49
12.	P. Parker	84	36
13.	I.C. Trueman	77	42
14.	F.H. Perring	70	49
15.	T.P. Diamond	63	45
16.	G. Potts	68	34
17.	E.D. Pugh	72	20
18.	M.J. Wigginton	65	24
19.	R.A. Dawes	66	20
20.	E.M. Rutter	44	39

William Leighton (1805-1889) recorded mostly between 1832 and 1841. He was a thoroughly reliable and careful botanist, and his notes on difficult genera such as *Fumaria* and *Epipactis* make interesting reading even today. His Flora, published in 1841, is still an invaluable source of information.

None of the contributors to Leighton's Flora make it into the top 20, although George Jorden (1783-1871), William Penny Brookes (1809-1895) and Thomas Salwey (1791-1877) come close, with 37, 20 and 29 records respectively.

William Phillips (1822-1905) made a significant contribution to the study of the flora of Shropshire in the 1870s, but he does not seem to have been a very original recorder. He produced the first list of ferns and fern allies for the county in 1877, mostly based on records collected by Leighton forty years earlier. He also published a list of plants of the Shrewsbury area in 1878. Leighton did apparently show him some of the plants *in situ*, but many of his records are obviously repeats of ones in Leighton's Flora.

William Beckwith (1844-1892), by contrast, was independent and thorough. His work was published in the Journal of Botany in three issues in the 1880s, and includes many significant new finds. Beckwith was originally an ornithologist, but he took on botanical responsibilities at a time when there were few active in this field in Shropshire.

Thomas Diamond (1839-1910) published his Flora of Oswestry in 1891 but it contains few, if any, of his own records. It is a compilation of work by local botanists, the most significant of whom was Oswald Moseley Feilden (1837-1924). Unfortunately, the names of the original recorders are rarely given so most are credited here to Diamond himself.

The 1890s and 1900s was a period of unprecedented activity. William Phillips Hamilton (1842-1910) and William Hunt Painter (1835-1910) were perhaps the most talented botanists of the time, and the county also received visits from such luminaries as Augustin Ley (1842-1911) and George Claridge Druce (1850-1932). A committee led by Hamilton got as far as producing a draft Flora by 1913, but it was never published, and the manuscript disappeared from Shrewsbury Library in the 1980s. Many of the records from that period are therefore lost.

The early decades of the 20th century were dominated by James Cosmo Melvill (1845-1929) and George Potts (1866-1945) who both enjoyed many years of recording. Potts continued to contribute for 41 years, making him one of the county's most prolific botanists.

Edward Rutter (1890-1963) retired to Shropshire in 1949, at a time when botany was at a low ebb. His main contribution was the publication of a Checklist, in collaboration with Llewelyn Cyril Lloyd (1905-1968) in 1957.

Charles Sinker moved to Shropshire in the late 1950s to work at the Field Studies Council, and was largely responsible for introducing the concept of ecology to the county. His Flora project was established in 1973 and led to publication of the *Ecological Flora* in 1985. It contains over 100,000 records collected by a large team of voluntary recorders. Species were recorded simply by 10km square if they were very common (A species); by tetrad if they were only moderately common (B species); or in full detail if they were perceived to be rare (C species).

Most of the records in Sinker's Flora are reliable, although there appear to be a few species that were perhaps over-recorded (Greater Burdock *Arctium lappa* and Orange Foxtail *Alopecurus aequalis* spring to mind). Despite considerable variation in the expertise of the recorders and the thoroughness with which they worked their squares, the end result is remarkably even coverage, geographically and taxonomically, which provides a very accurate baseline against which to measure future changes in the distribution of species.

Among the most reliable and prolific recorders in Sinker's Flora were Franklyn Perring (1927-2003), Doris Pugh (1910-1985), John Bingham, Chris Walker, Pat Parker and Ian Trueman.

Martin Wigginton led a team from the Nature Conservancy who surveyed several of the meres in 1979. Because individuals were not named, all the records are in Wigginton's name. It is interesting to note that a single season's recording can still earn a place in the top 20.

Since 1985 the Flora Group, which later became the Botanical Society, has continued to survey the county and collect records. Ian Trueman was the county recorder from 1976 to 1997, when Sarah Whild took on the rôle. Other currently active recorders in the top 20 include Kate Thorne, John Bingham, Rob Stokes and Ruth Dawes. A full list of all contributors is given on the following pages.

List of recorders & determiners

Mr G.D. Adams
Mr A. Aikin
Dr J.R. Akeroyd
Mr J. Alder
Mr W.B. Allen
Ms J. Allwood
Dr S.O.I. Almquist
Mr N. Anderson
Mr R. Anslow
Mr W. Anstice
Miss E. Armitage
Mrs A. Ashwell
Miss M.H. Asterley
Miss Attlee
Miss H.M. Auden
Mr H. Auden
Mr G.A. Audley
Mr S.J. Ayliffe
Rev. J. Babington
Prof. C.C. Babington
Mrs M. Badlan
Mr A. Bailey
Dr J.P. Bailey
Ms J.M. Baker
Mr J.S. Baly
V.A. Banbury
Dr H. Barnett
Mr R.M. Barrington
Prof. R.M. Bateman
Mr J.A. Bayley
Mr J. Baynes
Mr W. Beacall
Mr W.E. Beckwith
Mr A.P. Bell
Mr K.K. Bell
Dr D.J. Bellamy
Mr F.A. Bellamy
Mr A. Bennett
Mr P.M. Benoit
Mr E.B. Benson
Miss F.C. Benson
Mr R.deG. Benson
Sir P. Benthall
Mr G. Bentham
Mr J. Bevan
Mr S.H. Bickham
Dr H. Bidwell
Ms S. Bierley
Miss M.H. Bigwood
Mrs D. Bingham

Mr J. Bingham
Mr E. Birch
K.M. Bird
Rev. A. Bloxam
Mr A.G. Blunt
Mr T.P. Blunt
Mr P. Boardman
Mr T. Bodenham
Mrs M.A. Bodley
Mr I. Bolt
Mr R.A. Boniface
Mr I.R. Bonner
Mr W. Borrer
Mr J. Bowen
Dr G. Bowles
Mr J.E. Bowman
Dr J.D. Box
Mr P. Boyd
Ms H. Bramwell
Mr A. Breakwell
Mr S. Brewer
Mr J.D. Briggs
Dr W.P. Brookes
Miss Brown
Ms J. Brown
Rev. L. Brown
Mrs M. Bryant
Mr D.L. Buckingham
Rev. J. Burd
Dr R.C.L. Burges
Rev. W.T. Burges
Prof. Sir J.H. Burnett
Mr A.R. Busby
Mr R.W. Butcher
Mr S.G. Butler
Canon T. Butler
Rev. W. Butt
Miss D.A. Cadbury
Prof. R.A.D. Cameron
Mr B. Carleton
Ms A. Carter
Dr L. Carvalho
Ms G.E. Castle
Mr K.V. Cavalot
Mrs M.E. Chadd
Ms C. Chaffey
Mr J.H. Chandler
Dr S.B. Chapman
Rev. J.H.E. Charter
Mr A.O. Chater

Rev. G. Childe
Ms L.F. Chitty
Miss M. Chorley
J. Clark
Mr M.C. Clark
Rev. W.G. Clark-
  Maxwell
Mrs J.H. Clarke
Mr J. Clayfield
Mr E.J. Clement
Mr E. Cleminshaw
Mr E.S. Cobbold
Mrs A.T. Cole
Mrs W. Compson
Mrs M.J. Connell
Dr W.R.I. Cook
Mr J.E. Cooper
Rev. W. Coote
Mr S. Cope
Rev. W. Corbett
Mrs M. Cousins
Dr J.H.S. Cox
Mr T.A. Cox
Mr W.G. Cross
Rev. W.R. Crotch
Rev. J.F. Crouch
Mr A.A. Dallman
Mr J.E. Dandy
Mrs M.C. Daniel
Mr D. Daniels
Mrs K.E. Daniels
Mrs R.H. Dave
Dr R.W. David
Mr J. Alder
Ms H.M. Davidson
Mr G. Davies
Miss B. Davies
Mr M. Davies
Mrs C. Davies
Mr J. Davies
Mrs R.A. Dawes
Mr A.P. Dawes
Mr J.J. Day
Ms J. Deacon
Mrs M. Deadman
Mr I. Diack
Mr T.P. Diamond
Mr F. Dickinson
Prof. J.J. Dillenius
Mr J.F.M. Dovaston

Dr G.C. Druce
Dr T. Du Gard
Mr J.B. Duncan
Miss A. Dyer
Mrs J. Edwards
Dr R.J. Elliott
Mrs Ellis
Mr G. Ellis
Mrs S.A. Ellis
Mr E. Elsmere, jnr
Mrs D.M. Evans
Dr J. Evans
Mr T.C. Eyton
Mrs E. Farmer
Rev. O.M. Feilden
Mr S. Finch
Mr F. Fincher
Lady R. FitzGerald
Dr W.J. Fojt
Mr M.J.Y. Foley
Miss R. Ford
Mr H.E. Forrest
Mr B.R. Fowler
Ms A.R. Franks
Dr J. Fraser
Mr C. Fuller
J. Fuller
Miss M.B. Fuller
Mr G.M. Furley
Mr A.N. Gagg
Miss K.M. Gardner
Dr R. Garner
Mr P.S. Gateley
Dr M. Gepp
Mr A. Gepp
T.A. Gilmour
Sqn Ldr M. Godfrey
Mr K.M. Goodway
Mr M.E. Goodwin
Miss V. Gordon
Mrs R. Gore
Rev. G.G. Graham
Rev. J.D. Gray
Dr P.A. GreatRex
Mrs P.G. Green
M. A. Green
Mr R. Green
Mrs J. Greenhalgh
Dr G.H. Griffiths
Mr J. Groves

Recorders & determiners (cont.)

Mr D. Guest
Miss M.C. Hall
Mr W.P. Hamilton
Mr H. Hand
Dr D.J.L. Harding
Mr R. Harrison
Dr P.E. Hatcher
Mr D. Hatfield
Rev. J. Hayes
Ms K. Hayward
Mrs L.H. Hayward
Mr A. Hearle
Mr J.W. Heath
Mr D.J. Heaver
Mr A.T. Herbert
Mr B. Herring
Mrs E. Heywood-
   Waddington
Mr W.P. Hiern
Mr R.G. Higgins
Mrs M. Hignett
Mr A. Hillman
Mr M.G. Hoare
Mr N.G. Hodgetts
Mr T. Holland
Mr J.A. Hollier
Mr N.T.H. Holmes
Miss J.M. Hooson
Mr T.R. Horton
Mr A.R. Horwood
Rev. W.W. How
Mr M.J. Hudson
Mr H.H. Hughes
Dr H.V. Hughes
Mr T.A. Hulse
Mr P.F. Hunt
Mrs O. Hunter
Rev. Hutchinson
Mr Hutton
Mrs W.E. Hutton
Mr J. Ibbot
Mrs J. Ing
Mr R. Iremonger
Ms G.M. James
Mr J. James
Mr M. Jannick
Mr G.R. Jebb
Mrs R. Jefferson
Dr P. Jepson

Mr A.C. Jermy
Mr J. Jeudwine
Mr C. Johnson
Capt G.E. Johnson
Mr J.B. Johnson
Mr A. Jones
Miss E. Jones
H.L. Jones
Mr N. Jones
Mr W. Jones
Mrs Veronica Jones
Mrs Victoria Jones
Mr G. Jorden
Mr G.M. Kay
Mr R.G. Kemp
Ms S. Kilinc
Dr D.I. Kingham
Mr P. Kingsbury
Dr S. Kingsbury
Mrs E. Kirkham
Dr M.A.R. Kitchen
Mr G.D. Kitchener
Dr J.T.H. Knight
Mr P. Knights
Mrs E. Knowling
Rev. J.D. LaTouche
Rev. W.M.D.
   LaTouche
Mr A.R. Lamb
Mr D. Lambert
Mr R.V. Lansdown
Mr M. Lawley
Mr J.B. Lawson
Miss M.J. Lee
Mrs H.F. Pendlebury
Mr E. Lees
Miss R.B. Lees
Rev. W.A. Leighton
Miss Lewis
Rev. A. Ley
Mr E. Lhwyd
Dr E.M. Lind
Rev. E.F. Linton
Ms J.A. Lister
Miss Lloyd
Miss E.R. Lloyd
Dr G. Lloyd
Mr L.C. Lloyd
Mr J.E. Lousley

Mr R.S. Lucas
Mr P. Lukey
Ms T. MacLean
Miss N.M. Mackenzie
Mr J. Mallabar
Rev. S.P. Mansel
Mr R.J. Mantle
Mr St.J. Marriott
Rev. E.S. Marshall
Mr A. Marston
A. Martin
Mr J. Martin
Dr R.R. Martin
Mr D. Mason
Dr J.L. Mason
Mrs H. Matthews
Mr D.J. McCosh
Miss M. McGhie
Ms S.McGowan
Ms E.F. McKay
Mrs J. Mckelvey
Mr R.D. Meikle
Dr J.C. Melvill
Mr R. Melville
Mr R. Mileto
J. Mincher
Mrs T.E. Mitchell
Mr T. Moore
Ms V. Morgan
Prof. J.K. Morton
Miss H. Moseley
Dr B. Moss
Mr J.O. Mountford
Mr A. Muse
Mr E. Nelmes
Mr P.J.M. Nethercott
Dr C. Newbold
Rev. W.W. Newbould
Mr E. Newman
Mrs E. O'Donnell
Dr S. O'Donnell
Prof. D. Oliver
Miss Ormond
Mr P.H. Oswald
Mr J.H. Owen
Prof. J.R. Packham
Rev. W.H. Painter
Mrs D.E.M. Paish
Mr R.C. Palmer

Mr T.J. Pankhurst
Rev. J.A. Panter
Mrs P. Parker
Mr J.R. Parrott
Dr H.F. Parsons
Ms C.G.A. Paskell
Mr L.G. Payne
Mr D.A. Pearman
Mr W.H. Pearsall
Ms T. Pearson
Mr D. Pedlow
Mrs J. Pedlow
Miss Peele
Mrs H.F. Pendlebury
Mrs M. Perring
Dr F.H. Perring
Mr A.R. Perry
Mr K. Perry
Mr W.G. Perry
Rev. W. Phillips
Rev. G. Pinder
Mrs S. Pinsent
Miss F. Pitt
L.W. Poel
Mr T.F. Poole
Mr R.D. Porley
Mr M.S. Porter
Mrs B.E.H. Potter
Mrs E. Potts
Mr G. Potts
Mr C.B. Powell
Rev. E. Powell
Dr C.D. Preston
Mr W.V. Prestwood
Mrs S.R. Price
Mr W.R. Price
Ms B. Primrose
Dr M.C.F. Proctor
Miss E.D. Pugh
Mr H.W. Pugsley
Mrs J. Pursaill
Dr T. Purton
Dr O. Rackham
Mrs C. Raikes
Mrs J. Ramsbotham
Mr J. Ramsbottom
Mr G. Ransome
Ms J. Rapson
Ms A. Reed

Dr C.S. Reynolds
Dr T.C.G. Rich
Dr A.J. Richards
Mr G.P. Richards
Mr P. Richards
Mr W.E. Richards
Ms J. Rigby
Ms S. Roach
Miss J.A. Roberts
Mrs M.E. Roberts
Mr R.H. Roberts
Mr J.K. Rodwell
Rev. W.M. Rogers
Mrs J.M. Roper
Dr F. Rose
Mr R. Rowe
Dr F.J. Rumsey
Mr E.M. Rutter
Rev. T. Salwey
Rev. H. Sandford
Mr J. Sankey
Miss K.M. Saville
Rev. W.L. Scott
Dr B. Seddon
Mr P.D. Sell
Rev. E.R. Sequeira
Rev. R.M. Serjeantson
Mr D. Sharpe
Dr S.C. Shaw
Mr H.H. Shepherd
Dr W.A. Shoolbred
Mr R.F. Shoubridge
Dr A.J. Showler
Dr A.J. Silverside
Mr N.D. Simpson
Mr C.A. Sinker

Prof. A.D. Skelding
Mr W.J. Slack
Mr D. Smallshire
Ms J. Smith
Dr M.E. Smith
Mr R. Smith
Mr S. Smith
Mr L.M. Spalton
Mr H. Spare
Mr G.St.George Pool
Prof. C.A. Stace
Mrs S. Stafford
Prof. W.T. Stearn
Rev. Dr T. Stephenson
Mrs O.M. Stewart
Mr A.McG. Stirling
P.M. Stocks
Mr R.M. Stokes
Rev. H. Stokes
Mr G.M. Stone
Mr D. Stoves
Mr F. Stratton
Ms F.E. Strudwick
Mrs M.E. Sturt
Dr N. Sturt
Prof. G.A. Swan
Mr R.J. Swindells
Mrs S. Swindells
Ms C.E. Tandy
Dr P. Tattersfield
Sir G. Taylor
Mr P. Taylor
Ms T. Teearu
Rev. F.R. Tennant
Dr R. Thomas
Mr I.S. Thompson

Mrs J. Thompson
Mr J.A. Thompson
Rev. J.H. Thompson
Mr W.A. Thompson
Rev. W.E. Thompson
Dr A.K. Thorne
Mrs R. Thornes
Ms M. Thornton
Mr R.W. Tobin
Ms E. Townsend
Rev. J.M. Traherne
Prof. J.W.H. Trail
Prof. I.C. Trueman
Mr J.J. Tucker
Mr S.R. Turner
G.W. Turner
Miss H.M. Twigg
J. Vacey
Miss E. Vachell
Mr G. Vergine
Ms H. Vickers
Mrs M. Wainwright
Mrs P.H. Waite
Mr J. Walcot
Mr C. Walker
Mr R.M. Walls
Dr S.M. Walters
Dr E.F. Warburg
Mr C.W. Ward
Rev. R.H. Waring
Ms J.A. Warren
Mr W.W. Watkins
Mr H.C. Watson
Mr J.M. Way
Mr H. Webster
Mr D. Wells

Mr P. Welsh
Dr A. Welton
Dr C. West
Mr T. Westcombe
Mr F. Westcott
Mr B. Westwood
Mr A.W. Weyman
Dr D.B. Wheeler
Mr A. Whitbread
Mr A.E. White
Mr F.W. White
Miss K. White
Rev. E. Whitehead
Mr A. Whitehouse
Mr W. Whitwell
Dr M.J. Wigginton
Rev. E. Williams
Mrs E.A. Williams
Mrs M. Williams
Mr A.J. Wilmott
Mr E.A. Wilson
Mr G. Wilson
Dr T.W. Wilson
Dr W. Withering
Mr E.H. Wolfe
Dr P.A. Wolseley
Mr B.W. Wood
Ms D. Wood
Rev. W. Wood
Mr D.H. Wrench
Dr G. Wynne
Mr W. Yelland
Dr P.F. Yeo
Mrs D.M. Young
Dr D.P. Young

Changes in the flora

The most dramatic change to the flora occurs when a species goes extinct, but there is only one plant that has been recorded in Shropshire that might genuinely be lost to the world. That is Painter's Fumitory *Fumaria painteri*, which probably arose here by hybridisation, and then died out again fairly quickly.

Other species have apparently gone from the county, although they could of course come back from buried seed or by recolonisation from elsewhere. 'Extinction' is perhaps a rather dramatic word for these losses, but there doesn't seem to a better one, so it is used here to describe species that we believe are no longer found in the wild in the county. The list below shows the 48 native species (excluding hybrids, subspecies and critical taxa) that we believe have gone extinct.

Extinctions from v.c. 40

	Date of last record
Subularia aquatica	1805
Lycopodiella inundata	1849
Hornungia petraea	1855
Saxifraga hypnoides	1856
Dryopteris aemula	1858
Gymnocarpium robertianum	1864
Equisetum hyemale	1877
Potamogeton coloratus	1882
Scheuchzeria palustris	1884
Potamogeton gramineus	1885
Blysmus compressus	1886
Cephalanthera longifolia	1891
Juniperus communis	1891
Carex distans	1892
Epipogium aphyllum	1892
Isoetes lacustris	1893
Deschampsia setacea	1894
Hippuris vulgaris	1897
Myriophyllum verticillatum	1897
Utricularia vulgaris	1903
Orchis ustulata	1904
Fumaria painteri	1907
Listera cordata	1920
Lobelia dortmanna	1922
Juncus compressus	1924
Campanula glomerata	1935
Ophrys insectifera	1944
Antennaria dioica	1945
Carex diandra	1956
Cardamine impatiens	1959
Limosella aquatica	1962
Pilularia globulifera	1962
Carex limosa	1976
Hordeum secalinum	1978
Persicaria mitis	1979
Potamogeton lucens	1979
Hymenophyllum wilsonii	1984
Sparganium natans	1985
Gentianella campestris	1986
Diphasiastrum alpinum	1991
Rubus saxatilis	1991
Epipactis leptochila	1993
Potamogeton praelongus	1995
Baldellia ranunculoides	1996
Drosera anglica	1998
Drosera intermedia	1999
Potamogeton compressus	2002
Potamogeton friesii	2002

Climate change is one of the causes of extinction. Two hundred years ago Shropshire was just coming out of the Little Ice Age. Plants that had presumably survived here since the end of the last major glaciation 15,000 years ago would have been thriving. Since then the climate has become quite unsuitable for species such as Rannoch-rush *Scheuchzeria palustris* and Awlwort *Subularia aquatica*.

Drainage of wetlands was another early cause of extinctions. Much of north Shropshire was once wet, with the Weald Moors covering large parts of the east, and valley mires along the Morda, Perry, Roden and Tern occupying vast areas in the west. Between the river catchments were numerous meres and mosses, some of which have been completely drained and eradicated from the maps. The pondweeds *Potamogeton coloratus*, *gramineus* and *lucens* are among the casualties of this activity, as is Mare's-tail *Hippuris vulgaris*.

Amelioration of the climate coincided with improved transport at the end of the eighteenth century, firstly with the canals and then the railways. This stimulated a change from sheep farming to dairying as the dominant land use in north Shropshire, and brought the first effects of eutrophication. Agricultural intensification has continued to the present day, complementing the effects of warmer weather and drainage by eliminating the low nutrient habitats. Flat Sedge *Blysmus compressus* and Clustered Bellflower *Campanula glomerata* are among the casualties.

Changing agricultural practice led to the abandonment of many small-scale quarries and the practice of lime burning, which may have been responsible for the highly calcareous soils that supported the likes of Burnt Orchid *Orchis ustulata* and Fly Orchid *Ophrys insectifera*.

Another significant cause of change is development - industrialisation and urbanisation. Recent losses include Alpine Clubmoss *Diphasiastrum alpinum*, which was destroyed during the creation of a landfill site. The redevelopment of the canal network for motorised boats has caused the extinction of several species of aquatic plants, including the pondweeds *Potamogeton compressus* and *P. friesii*.

One of the biggest causes of loss in recent years has been natural succession on nature reserves. These sites are often selected because they contain rare plants, but there is little evidence that it is an effective way to preserve them. Succession to scrub and ultimately to dense woodland within reserves is probably the main cause of the loss of the sundews *Drosera anglica* and *D. intermedia*, Least Bur-reed *Sparganium natans* and Lesser Water-plantain *Baldellia ranunculoides*.

The graph below shows the average rate of extinction of species in Shropshire over the last 200 years. It seems that there is a clear upward trend from about one species every

25 years to nearly one every two years now. This seems set to continue, with quite a few species on the verge of extinction. Red Pondweed *Potamogeton alpinus* is now down to just one tiny population, established in an off-line reserve adjacent to the Montgomery Canal at Aston Locks. Field Garlic *Allium oleraceum* is equally vulnerable in its last site along Blakeway Hollow, where the hedges have become overgrown and eutrophicated in recent years. The reason may be that there is now no movement of livestock along this ancient trackway, as the fields above are all arable. Spreading Bellflower *Campanula patula* is also heading towards extinction, with just three or four sites remaining in the county. Marsh Gentian *Gentiana pneumonanthe* is another plant of nature reserves that cannot withstand the succession to scrub, and Green-flowered Helleborine *Epipactis phyllanthes* may already be gone, due to the under-management of woodlands.

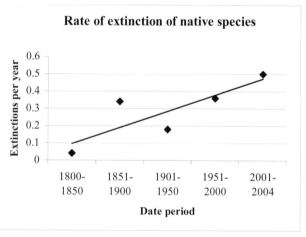

The loss of many of the county's native species is partly offset by the arrival of new plants from elsewhere in Britain and abroad. There is a trend of northerly, wetland plants being replaced by southerly species of ruderal habitats. Round-leaved Crane's-bill *Geranium rotundifolium* and Grass Vetchling *Lathyrus nissolia* are two arguably native species that seem to have colonised the county recently.

Sites

If you calculate the number of rare native species ever recorded at each site in the county, Bomere Pool (SJ4908) comes out top of the list. Analysis of tetrads gives the same result, so this is not just an artefact of site recording.

Bomere Pool is (or was) a truly extraordinary site, with a large mesotrophic lake surrounded by fen, mire, ancient woodland and calcareous grassland. Among the rarest plants found there in the past was Rannoch Rush *Scheuchzeria palustris*.

Water quality in the mere has remained remarkably good and it is now the only natural water body left in lowland England with a native population of Floating Water-plantain *Luronium natans*. It is probably the best preserved of all the meres, with Six-stamened Waterwort *Elatine hexandra* also still present. At nearby Shomere Pool (SJ5007) (No. 14 on the list, but in a different tetrad) there is abundant Marsh Fern *Thelypteris palustris* and Royal Fern *Osmunda regalis*. The Bomere/Shomere complex is privately owned and managed as a leisure activities centre, which seems to have served it well, but there is no public access except by permission.

The Mere at Ellesmere (SJ4034) was, historically, almost as rich a site as Bomere, coming second in both the site and the tetrad lists. Its most important feature was the presence of an extensive raised mire immediately adjacent to a base-rich lake. It, too, once had *Scheuchzeria palustris* and *Luronium natans*. The construction of the Montgomery Canal in about 1800 was probably what triggered its destruction, with the drainage of The Moors and the stabilisation of the water level to prevent flooding. There is now very little to be seen at The Mere, although Needle Spike-rush *Eleocharis acicularis* still survives on a part of the shore that is privately owned. Much of the lake and its surrounds is managed by Shropshire County Council and is open to the public, but its management is neglected and the remaining areas of good habitat have turned to scrub over the last thirty years or so.

Shropshire's best sites for rare species

		No. of rare species	
		Ever	…now
1.	Bomere Pool	29	3
2.	The Mere, Ellesmere	28	2
3.	Wyre Forest	23	10
4.	Cole Mere	22	4
5.	Wenlock Edge	21	6
6.	Crose Mere	18	5
7.	The Long Mynd	16	7
8.	Titterstone Clee	15	10
9.	Brown Moss	14	4
10.	Rednal Moss	14	0
11.	White Mere	14	4
12.	Montgomery Canal	13	2
13.	Blake Mere	12	1
14.	Shomere Pool	12	3
15.	Earl's Hill	11	7
16.	Hencott Pool	11	3
17.	Shawbury Heath	11	0
18.	Wem Moss	11	3
19.	Berrington Pool	10	3
20.	Blodwel Rocks	10	4
21.	Clarepool Moss	10	1
22.	The Stiperstones	10	3

The Wyre Forest (SO7576) is an extensive area of woodland and grassland straddling the boundary between Shropshire and Worcestershire. Although the larger part is in this county, most of the nature reserves and several of the more interesting plants (including Narrow-leaved Helleborine *Cephalanthera longifolia*) are on the other side. There has been much afforestation, although some good stands of ancient woodland remain, and there are currently plans to restore large areas to broadleaf woodland. Among the rarities there are Soft-leaved Sedge *Carex montana*, Mountain Melick *Melica nutans* and Wood Crane's-bill *Geranium sylvaticum*. Because it is such a large area, it does not figure so highly in the map of tetrads.

Cole Mere (SJ4333) is now a country park, managed by the County Council, and there is public access to the entire shoreline. Its chief claim to fame is Least Water-lily *Nuphar pumila* at its only native site in England.

Unfortunately, over the last thirty years or so the edges of the lake have become wooded, and the water-lily is now on the verge of extinction. Just one small population survives in the north-west corner. Elongated Sedge *Carex elongata*, however, has thrived in the alder carr and is abundant along the north shore, and Annual Water-starwort *Callitriche hermaphroditica* still occurs on the open part of the shoreline near the boathouse.

The largest area of limestone in Shropshire is at Wenlock Edge. It was once a good area for arable weeds such as Red Hemp-nettle *Galeopsis angustifolia* and plants of calcareous grassland such as Frog Orchid *Coeloglossum viride*, but these species-rich habitats are now almost gone.

Coincidence map of rare species

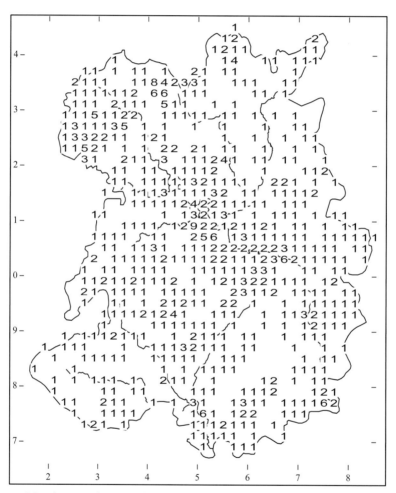

Numbers on the map show the number of rare species that have been recorded in each tetrad, using a scale from 1 (1-5 species) to 9 (41-47 species).

The problem with Wenlock Edge now is that it consists of fenced-off stands of high forest sandwiched between intensive farmland and quarries, which between them only support a few of the rare species that used to occur. An interesting example is Blakeway Hollow (SO6099), where unmanaged hedgerows are shading out such species as Field Garlic

Rare Plants of Shropshire

Allium oleraceum and Cat-mint *Nepeta cataria* from their last sites in the county. Much of the woodland on Wenlock Edge is owned by the National Trust and is open to the public; but many of the rarities, including Basil Thyme *Clinopodium acinos*, Venus's Looking-glass *Legousia hybrida* and Dwarf Thistle *Cirsium acaule*, are found only on private land.

Crose Mere, Sweat Mere & Whattal Moss (SJ4330) together make up what once must have been a superb wetland that included raised mire, a base-rich lake and ancient woodland. The area was drained by several metres about 200 years ago, and Sweat Mere and Whattal Moss have since been largely afforested. Almost the whole area is fenced off and turning to scrub, and rare species continue to be lost at a startling rate. The north shore of Crose Mere is still largely open, however, and this is the only site in the county where Great Fen-sedge *Cladium mariscus* still occurs in some abundance.

Titterstone Clee (SO5977) has lost few of its rarities, so although it comes eighth in the table of best sites ever, it rises to joint first place (with the Wyre Forest) if the analysis is repeated using just the post-1994 records. It is particularly important as the most south-easterly outpost of some of the montane flora of north-west Britain, with such species as Fir Clubmoss *Huperzia selago*, Parsley Fern *Cryptogramma crispa*, and Mountain Male Fern *Dryopteris oreades*. It is mostly common land and is open to the public.

Brown Moss (SJ5639) is interesting because many species that were once widespread in the meres and mosses survived longer at this site than elsewhere. Unfortunately, they seem to have disappeared in the last decade or so, and the rare plants still there, such as Small Water-pepper *Persicaria minor*, Orange Foxtail *Alopecurus aequalis* and Nodding Bur-marigold *Bidens cernua* var. *radiata* are tolerant of eutrophic conditions.

Rednal Moss (SJ3427) was once a fine raised mire (here taken to include Twyford Vownog), but it was drained when the Montgomery Canal came through in about 1800, and no longer has any rare plants.

White Mere (SJ4132) has a suite of species typical of the meres, but nothing very special.

The Montgomery Canal was once one of the finest canals in Britain for aquatic vegetation. Most notably, it had until recently three rare species of pondweed as well as Floating Water-plantain. Unfortunately, it has lost almost all its aquatic plants as a consequence of its redevelopment for modern leisure boating, and there does not seem to be any way (or will) to reconcile boating with the nature conservation importance of canals.

Blake Mere (SJ4133) and Hencott Pool (SJ4916) are two more meres that have suffered from succession to woodland. Neither is of any particular interest in its current state.

Earl's Hill (SJ4004) is the Wildlife Trust's finest nature reserve, with a host of interesting plants, including Mountain Male-fern *Dryopteris oreades* and Upland Enchanter's-nightshade *Circaea ˣintermedia*. There is convenient parking near Pontesbury and good public access. Since the reserve was established the Trust has managed to maintain the main areas of grassland by sheep grazing, but the most important areas – the cliffs and screes – have largely succeeded to woodland, and characteristic species such as Rock Stonecrop *Sedum forsterianum* are becoming very rare.

Shawbury Heath (SJ5420) is now an airfield and farmland, and the last rare plant record for there was in 1942. It would, however, be an interesting place for an agricultural extensification programme, given the sandy soils.

Wem Moss (SJ4734) is another Wildlife Trust reserve. It is a sizeable peat bog – the southernmost part of the Whixall Moss complex. Unfortunately, it has dried out significantly, and is now mostly woodland and scrub. Royal Fern *Osmunda regalis*, Bog Myrtle *Myrica gale* and White Beak-sedge *Rhynchospora alba* still remain, but the list of rare species there is rapidly getting shorter. There is a footpath around the moss, but access is difficult due to the dense vegetation.

Berrington Pool (SJ5207) is a typical mere that is most notable for its Slender Sedge

Carex lasiocarpa. Blodwel Rocks (SJ2622) is a limestone escarpment with some ancient woodland, but also a lot of plantation. Both have public footpaths. Clarepool Moss was once a fabulous raised mire (the last site for Bog Sedge *Carex limosa*) but is now mostly dense bracken and woodland, to which there is no public access.

The Stiperstones (SO3698) is a large area of upland moorland with a thin scattering of rare species such as Stag's-horn Clubmoss *Lycopodium clavatum* and Hybrid Bilberry *Vaccinium* ^{x}*intermedium*. It is all open to the public and is managed by English Nature as a National Nature Reserve.

Nature conservation

Rare plants are of some interest to nature conservation, but not necessarily in the ways that one would expect. They are almost invariably on the edge of their range where they are rare, and sometimes they seem almost bound to go extinct, whatever is done to protect them. In other cases, careful management of their habitat can help, and this is often the focus of conservation activities. In almost all cases, however, rare plants are primarily useful in demonstrating what the habitat was like in the past, and in the case of native Salopian plants that usually means the cold, wet, nutrient-poor postglacial past, even though there have been times since the last glaciation when the climate was warmer than it is now. With the exception of a few endemics, all these rarities are still common elsewhere, and although it is important to preserve them on the edge of their range, this is always going to be a difficult task.

A far more important objective of nature conservation is to maintain a healthy and dynamic ecosystem with clean air, pure water and healthy soils. This is to the benefit of both humans and wildlife, and does not necessarily have to be associated with any particular period in the past. To monitor the state of the environment, in terms of pollution levels, habitat structure and complexity, water clarity, and intensity of land use, the rare plants are not particularly useful. They can be eradicated by chance events that do not reflect trends, or they can be planted or accidentally introduced – which does not reflect in any way a gain for nature conservation. A far more appropriate suite of species to monitor are the habitat indicator species. These can occur in many sites throughout the county, but are nearly always indicators of the better types of habitat, and are probably associated with other desirable environmental features such as the diversity of insects, or unpolluted water.

A list of suggested Indicator Species for Shropshire is given below. Unlike the rare plants, these are the 'nature conservation' species of importance in the county. It is possible to devise measures such as the number of such species that need to be present in a site for it to qualify for protected status. We can also monitor trends in the environment by measuring the distribution and abundance of these species. It is a complex task, involving the manipulation of large amounts of data, but it is becoming increasingly practical as the technology improves. The species below only count as indicators if they have not been planted and are in an appropriate habitat. The list includes a few species that have probably become extinct in the county in recent years, but not those that disappeared decades or centuries ago.

Habitat Indicator Species in Shropshire

Acer campestre
Achillea ptarmica
Aconitum napellus
Adoxa moschatellina
Aira caryophyllea
A. praecox
Alchemilla filicaulis ssp. vestita
A. glabra
A. xanthochlora
Alisma lanceolatum
Allium oleraceum
Alopecurus aequalis
Anacamptis pyramidalis
Anagallis minima
A. tenella
Anchusa arvensis
Andromeda polifolia
Anemone nemorosa
Anthemis cotula
Anthriscus caucalis
Anthyllis vulneraria
Apium inundatum
Astragalus glycyphyllos
Astrantia major
Berula erecta
Bidens cernua var. radiata
Blackstonia perfoliata
Blechnum spicant
Botrychium lunaria
Briza media
Bromopsis benekenii
B. erecta
B. ramosa
Bromus racemosus
Butomus umbellatus
Calamagrostis canescens
Callitriche hermaphroditica
Campanula glomerata
C. latifolia
C. patula
C. amara
C. impatiens
Carduus tenuiflorus
Carex acuta
C. binervis
C. caryophyllea
C. curta
C. digitata
C. dioica
C. disticha
C. echinata
C. elata
C. elongata
C. hostiana
C. laevigata
C. lasiocarpa

C. montana
C. muricata ssp. muricata
C. pallescens
C. paniculata
C. pilulifera
C. pseudocyperus
C. pulicaris
C. rostrata
C. spicata
C. strigosa
C. vesicaria
C. viridula ssp. brachyrrhyncha
C. viridula ssp. oedocarpa
C. viridula ssp. viridula
Carlina vulgaris
Catabrosa aquatica
Catapodium rigidum
Centaurea cyanus
C. scabiosa
Cerastium diffusum
C. semidecandrum
Ceratocapnos claviculata
Chrysanthemum segetum
Chrysosplenium alternifolium
Cicuta virosa
Circaea ˣintermedia
Cirsium acaule
C. dissectum
C. eriophorum
Cladium mariscus
Clinopodium acinos
C. ascendens
C. vulgare
Coeloglossum viride
Colchicum autumnale
Convallaria majalis
Crataegus laevigata
Crepis paludosa
Cryptogramma crispa
Cystopteris fragilis
Dactylorhiza incarnata
D. maculata
D. praetermissa
D. purpurella
Daphne laureola
Dianthus deltoides
Diphasiastrum alpinum
Dipsacus pilosus
Drosera anglica
D. intermedia
D. rotundifolia
Dryopteris carthusiana
D. oreades
Echium vulgare
Elatine hexandra
Eleocharis acicularis

E. multicaulis
E. quinqueflora
Eleogiton fluitans
Empetrum nigrum
Epipactis helleborine
E. leptochila
E. palustris
E. phyllanthes
E. purpurata
Equisetum sylvaticum
Erigeron acer
Eriophorum angustifolium
E. latifolium
E. vaginatum
Erodium maritimum
E. moschatum
Erophila glabrescens
E. majuscula
E. verna
Euonymus europaeus
Euphorbia amygdaloides
Euphrasia officinalis agg.
Festuca altissima
Filago minima
Filipendula vulgaris
Frangula alnus
Fumaria capreolata
F. purpurea
Gagea lutea
Galeopsis angustifolia
G. speciosa
Galium odoratum
G. uliginosum
Genista anglica
G. tinctoria
Gentiana pneumonanthe
Gentianella amarella
G. campestris
Geranium columbinum
G. sanguineum
G. sylvaticum
Geum rivale
Gnaphalium sylvaticum
Gymnadenia conopsea
Gymnocarpium dryopteris
Helianthemum nummularium
Helictotrichon pubescens
Helleborus foetidus
H. viridis
Hieracium cinderella
H. lasiophyllum
Hippuris vulgaris
Hordelymus europaeus
Hordeum secalinum
Hottonia palustris

Indicator Species (contd.)

Huperzia selago
Hyacinthoides non-scripta
Hydrocharis morsus-ranae
Hymenophyllum wilsonii
Hypericum elodes
H. montanum
H. pulchrum
Hypochaeris glabra
Impatiens noli-tangere
Inula conyzae
Iris foetidissima
Isolepis setacea
Jasione montana
Juncus foliosus
J. subnodulosus
Juniperus communis
Kickxia elatine
Lamiastrum galeobdolon
Lamium amplexicaule
L. hybridum
Lathraea squamaria
Lathyrus linifolius
L. sylvestris
Legousia hybrida
Lepidium campestre
Linum catharticum
Listera ovata
Lithospermum arvense
L. officinale
Littorella uniflora
Luronium natans
Luzula multiflora
L. pilosa
L. sylvatica
Lycopodium clavatum
Lysimachia vulgaris
Lythrum portula
Melampyrum pratense
Melica nutans
M. uniflora
Menyanthes trifoliata
Milium effusum
Moenchia erecta
Monotropa hypopitys
Myosotis discolor
M. ramosissima
M. secunda
Myrica gale
Myriophyllum alterniflorum
Narcissus pseudonarcissus
Narthecium ossifragum
Neottia nidus-avis
Nuphar pumila
Oenanthe aquatica
O. crocata

O. fistulosa
Ononis repens
O. spinosa
Ophioglossum vulgatum
Ophrys apifera
Orchis mascula
O. morio
Oreopteris limbosperma
Origanum vulgare
Ornithopus perpusillus
Orobanche rapum-genistae
Osmunda regalis
Oxalis acetosella
Papaver argemone
P. hybridum
Paris quadrifolia
Parnassia palustris
Pedicularis palustris
P. sylvatica
Persicaria minor
Phegopteris connectilis
Pimpinella saxifraga
Pinguicula vulgaris
Plantago coronopus
P. media
Platanthera bifolia
P. chlorantha
Poa compressa
Polygala serpyllifolia
Polypodium cambricum
Polystichum aculeatum
P. setiferum
Potamogeton alpinus
P. compressus
P. friesii
P. obtusifolius
P. polygonifolius
P. praelongus
Potentilla argentea
P. palustris
Prunus padus
Pulicaria dysenterica
Pyrola minor
Ranunculus auricomus
R. circinatus
R. fluitans
R. lingua
R. omiophyllus
R. parviflorus
R. peltatus
R. penicillatus
R. sardous
R. trichophyllus
Rhamnus cathartica
Rhinanthus minor

Rhynchospora alba
Rosa micrantha
R. obtusifolia
R. spinosissima
Rubus saxatilis
Rumex maritimus
Sagina nodosa
Sagittaria sagittifolia
Salix aurita
S. ˣmultinervis
S. pentandra
S. purpurea
S. repens
Samolus valerandi
Sanguisorba minor
S. officinalis
Sanicula europaea
Saxifraga tridactylites
Scabiosa columbaria
Scandix pecten-veneris
Schoenoplectus tabernaemontani
Scirpus sylvaticus
Scleranthus annuus
Scrophularia umbrosa
Scutellaria minor
Sedum forsterianum
Senecio aquaticus
Serratula tinctoria
Sherardia arvensis
Silaum silaus
Solidago virgaurea
Sorbus anglica
S. torminalis
Sparganium natans
Spiranthes spiralis
Spirodela polyrhiza
Stachys arvensis
S. officinalis
S. palustris
Stellaria pallida
S. palustris
Teesdalia nudicaulis
Thalictrum flavum
Thelypteris palustris
Thymus pulegioides
Tilia cordata
T. platyphyllos
Torilis nodosa
Trichophorum cespitosum
Trifolium campestre
T. micranthum
T. striatum
Triglochin palustre
Triseteum flavescens

Indicator Species (contd.)

Trollius europaeus
Typha angustifolia
Ulmus minor
U. plotii
U. procera
Utricularia minor
U. vulgaris
Vaccinium ˣintermedium
V. oxycoccos

V. vitis-idaea
Valeriana dioica
Valerianella dentata
V. eriocarpa
Veronica anagallis-aquatica
V. catenata
V. montana
V. scutellata
Vicia lathyroides

V. sylvatica
Viola canina
V. lutea
V. palustris
V. reichenbachiana
Wahlenbergia hederacea
Zannichellia palustris

Coincidence map of Indicator Species

Analysis of 49,000 records of indicator species showing the number of taxa ever recorded in each tetrad. The smallest dots have between 1 and 13 species, and largest dots are for tetrads with up to 117 indicator species present.

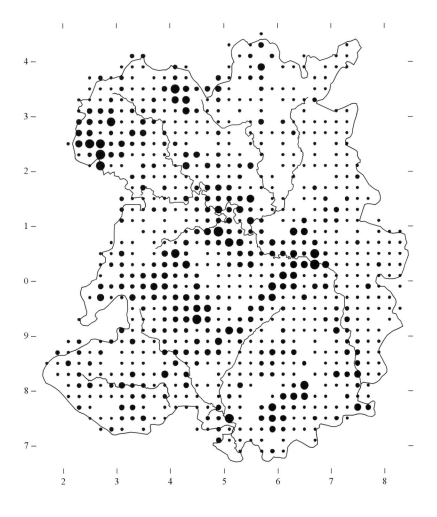

Species Accounts

For each species, the current scientific and common names are given, followed by its status in the county. Then there is a description of its recorded history, generally starting with the oldest known sites and working through to the most recent. Notes are given on the distribution or status beyond Shropshire where this is useful but, given the number of Atlases and guides now available, no attempt has been made to cover this subject comprehensively. Almost all records are given in full, with the site name (where there have been changes the modern name is normally used), year and recorder (often just the surname for the more prolific botanists). Unconfirmed and erroneous records are often given in the text but do not appear on the maps. If a species is thought not to have been correctly recorded in the county, the name is enclosed by square brackets. Species with more than a few sites are mapped using tetrad dots, with open circles for pre-1995 records and black dots for 1995 onwards.

Aconitum napellus L.

Monk's-hood

Archaeophyte. Scarce.

Monk's-hood has been cultivated in Britain as a medicinal herb for thousands of years. It is also now grown as an ornamental, and it is a common and widespread garden escape throughout Britain, being recorded in over 600 hectads in the New Atlas. There are thought to be three taxa: a putative native subspecies *A. napellus* ssp. *napellus*, which occurs naturally only in western England and southern Wales; an introduced European subspecies *A. napellus* ssp. *vulgare*, which is widespread; and a garden hybrid, *A. ×cammarum*, which is thought to be under-recorded. All three are widely cultivated.

Edward Whitehead (1789-1827) is widely credited (e.g. Clarke 1900, Desmond 1994) with the discovery of 'truly wild' Monk's-hood in Britain, which he found growing along the Ledwyche Brook at the base of the Iron Age hill fort of Caynham Camp (SO5473) in 1819; but it seems that Edward Williams and Joseph Babington had both recorded it there some 20 years earlier, and Leighton (1841) dismissed it as an introduction. This debate is still quite unresolved, and there is a case for it to be viewed as a native, archaeophyte or neophyte. Joseph Babington's comment (in Plymley, 1803) is delicately worded: 'This plant, which is now, I believe, allowed to be indigenous, grows in an apparently wild state, in some places within a few miles of Ludlow.'

Whatever its status, it is still present along some of the tributaries of the Teme. For instance, John Akeroyd has recorded it as native along the Seifton Brook in Seifton Bache (SO4784, 1989). Elsewhere in the county it is almost certainly a garden escape. It is difficult to be certain how many putatively native populations there may be, but it is quite possibly fewer than ten.

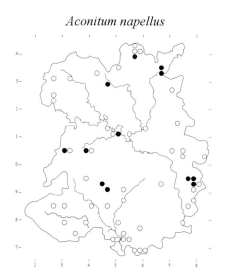

Aconitum napellus

Agrostemma githago L.

Corncockle

Archaeophyte. Rare.

Corncockle was once a serious agricultural pest, contaminating cereal crops with its bitter seeds. In 1841 Leighton considered it too common to record, so the first localised record of it in the county was in 1849 (in cornfields at Whitchurch, SJ5441,

H. Sandford). It seems to have been eliminated from crops in the late 19th century, as most of the more recent records for it are as a casual; for instance George Potts found it in a chicken run at Tickwood (SJ6402) in 1929. It is sometimes assumed that it only occurs now when introduced with a wild flower mix, but it does also come up from buried seed. Rob Stokes found some such plants in Donnington (SJ7014) in 1994, but other recent sightings for the Monkmoor bypass (SJ5011, John Martin, 1990) and Snailbeach (SJ3701, Sarah Whild, 1996) are more likely to have been of plants introduced by local authorities.

Alisma lanceolatum With.
Narrow-leaved water-plantain
Native. Scarce.

Edward Williams first recorded this species in about 1800, at Sundorne Pool (SJ5215). It was not recorded again in the county until 1895, when William Hunt Painter found it in the Coalport Canal at Madeley (SJ6903). It was still there in 1975 when Frank Perring refound it at Blists Hill (SJ6902), and it was later seen there by Bill Thompson (1982), John Box (1986), and Lockton & Whild (1995). It has since disappeared because the canal was not well maintained, but it could conceivably come back from the seed bank.

Apart from Williams's, there are just two other records of this plant in habitats other than canals. A specimen from Walcot Pool (SO3485) was used as the basis of an illustration by Florence Strudwick in 1930; and in 1995 it was collected from the banks of the River Roden at Spenford Bridge (SJ4729, Lockton). These raise the possibility that it could be more widespread, but that is unproven.

The best-known site for it is the Montgomery Canal. It was first recorded there by John Alder at Aston Locks (SJ3225 & SJ3326) in 1985, and has since been seen there by Lockton, Lansdown & Whild (1995–1997) and Newbold (2001). Richard Lansdown also found it in 1997 at Berghill Farm (SJ3629), Crickheath Bridge (SJ2823), Heath Houses (SJ3427), Keeper's Bridge (SJ3528), Llanymynech (SJ2721), Lockgate Bridge

(SJ3630), Maesbury Marsh (SJ3124), the Rednal Basin (SJ3527) and Queen's Head (SJ3326). Newbold saw it at the latter site in 2001 and recorded it in the Aston Locks reserve (SJ3326) in 2003. Following the re-opening of the Montgomery Canal in 2003, however, it is uncertain how many of these populations survive.

Other canals in which it has been found are the Shrewsbury Canal (SJ5114, Whild & Lockton, 1995) and a derelict stretch of canal in Granville Country Park (SJ7112, Stokes, 1997).

Alisma lanceolatum

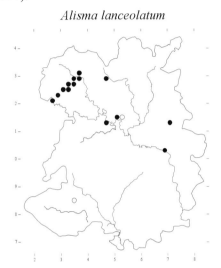

Allium oleraceum L.
Field Garlic
Native. Rare.

This species has always been rare in the county. George Jorden recorded it in the Wyre Forest in 1856, but did not say on which side of the county boundary he had seen it. Otherwise, the first record was in 1880, when William Beckwith found it by the road from Cressage (SJ5904) to Cound Moor (SJ5502). A dot for SJ42 (1950+) in the 1962 Atlas is unsubstantiated. In 1977 Winifred Hutton found it in a field at High Grosvenor (SO7793), but this site was ploughed by 1986. In 1973 Mary Fuller recorded it in Blakeway Hollow (SO6099), on Wenlock Edge, and there were about 25 plants in 2001 (Whild & Lockton). This remains the only known site for it in the county. *A. oleraceum* is a plant of dry, unimproved calcareous grassland. In the past it was considered an introduction to Britain, but in the New Atlas it is listed as native in 145 squares. It is most common in Worcestershire and the lower Severn Valley, and northwards from Derbyshire to the Scottish border.

Alopecurus aequalis Sobol.
Orange Foxtail
Native. Rare.

From the records given in Sinker's Flora, it appears that this species has suffered a dramatic decline, but there are doubts about the validity of some of them. Because it was considered a reasonably common plant, the majority of records are anonymous tetrad dots without any supporting evidence. They are probably best ignored, but it is impossible to say for sure that they are erroneous.

The only place in Shropshire where *A. aequalis* has been recorded more than once is Brown Moss, where it was discovered by Charles Sinker in 1961 and has since been seen by numerous botanists. Sarah Whild found it to be abundant around pools 1, 4 & 5 in 2002. The only other wild site for it is a small kettlehole mere in Attingham Park, where Frank Perring recorded it in about 1972, but it has not been seen there again. In 2004 Pete Boardman found it in his garden pond in Weston Rhyn (SJ2835) but its provenance is unknown.

A. aequalis occurs on the margins of fluctuating mesotrophic water bodies in the OV35 *Lythrum portula-Ranunculus flammula* community, which was once characteristic of some of the meres but is now almost lost from the county as a result of eutrophication and succession to scrub. It can also occur in highly eutrophic conditions in agricultural landscapes, but has not been observed in this habitat in Shropshire. Its wide tolerance of trophic status may account for its continued presence at Brown Moss.

Alopecurus myosuroides Huds.
Black-grass
Archaeophyte. Scarce.

This species is typically an agricultural weed in the south-east of Britain, but it reaches the edge of its range in Shropshire and is more commonly found as a casual on roadsides. In the 18th century Edward Williams recorded it in cornfields between Culmington and Onibury (ca. SO4780), by the side of the road at Ditton Priors (SO6089), and at Nash (SO6071) and Harnage (SJ5604). In Leighton's Flora (1841) there are records for Oakly Park (SO4876, Spare) and a 'field south of Ludlow, on the Leominster road' (SO5173, Bowman). In 1894 Painter recorded it at Stirchley (SJ7006) and in 1895 E.B. Benson collected it near Baschurch (SJ4221).

During Sinker's Flora project it was found just three times: Bryan Fowler recorded it in a field margin at Harriot's Hayes (SJ8305, 1976) and on a road verge at Rudge Heath (SO8095, 1977), and Henry Hand recorded it as a casual in a garden at Alcaston (SO4687) in 1977. In 1979 Martin Wigginton found it at Fenemere (SJ4422), where it was subsequently seen by Whild & Walker in 1996.

Since then it seems to have been on the increase, and it may now be quite frequent along roadsides. There are records for Bishops Castle (SO3288, Trueman, 1988); the Shrewsbury Ring Road at Monkmoor (SJ5011, John Martin, 1990); a field corner at Ercall Mill Bridge (SJ5816, Mark Lawley & Jon Mallabar, 1999), a grassy verge in Trench (SJ6912, Whild, 2004) and a roadside at Crudgington (SJ6318, Whild, 2004).

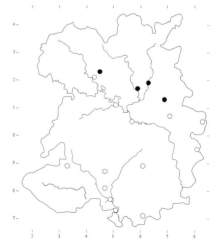

Alopecurus myosuroides

Anagallis minima (L.) E.H. Krause
Chaffweed
Native. Rare.

This is a plant of bare, damp, sandy ground on heaths and woodland rides. It was discovered in the Wyre Forest in 1882 by R.M. Serjeantson and W.E. Beckwith, but was not recorded there again until John Bingham rediscovered it in 1991. It has now been seen in about ten distinct localities on the Shropshire side of the border, in Wimperhill Wood (SO7376 & SO7476) and Skeys Wood (SO7677 & SO7777) by John Bingham and Brett Westwood. A record for Haughmond Hill (SJ5414) by Allan McGregor Stirling in 1958 has never been repeated.

Anagallis minima

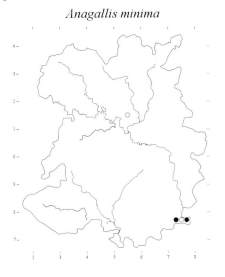

Antennaria dioica (L.) Gaertn.
Mountain Everlasting
Native. Extinct (1945).

Although this is a common and widespread species on hills and mountains in the north and west, it has declined almost to extinction in the lowlands of England.

Turner & Dillwyn (1805) gave a record for it 'on the road from Trebrodind (possibly Trebrodier, SO2080) to Clun,' but it has not been recorded in that part of the county again. In 1891 Diamond listed it as occurring on Llanymynech Hill (SJ2622), but whether in Shropshire or Montgomeryshire he 'does not say. It has subsequently been recorded on the

Welsh side of the border many times, but not in Shropshire. Ellen Lloyd discovered it on Llynclys Hill (SJ2723) in 1926, where she saw it again in 1932 and where J.H. Owen recorded it in 1945. The site was apparently at Jacob's Ladder, close to the Welsh border but definitely on the English side.

Anthemis arvensis L.
Corn Chamomile
Archaeophyte. Rare.

Leighton recorded this species in cereal fields at Battlefield (SJ5116) and Hencott Pool (SJ4916) in about 1841, and in his Flora he gives a record by Henry Spare for Oakly Park (SO4876) which should probably be considered unconfirmed. In 1870 Griffith Griffiths also dubiously recorded it at Cardington (SO5095) and Minton (SO4390). William Phillips (1878) listed the same sites as Leighton, and although he did make new records for many species, it seems possible that he was just repeating the old ones on this occasion. Diamond (1891) lists it as frequent in the Oswestry district, which again seems rather doubtful.

Anthemis arvensis

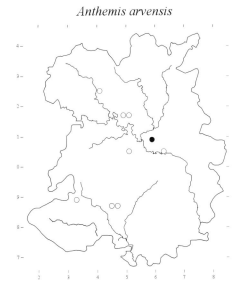

William Hunt Painter's record for Bishop's Castle (SO3288, 1896) is reliable, as are those of W.B. Allen, George Potts and J.C. Melvill of it as a casual on waste ground at Buildwas (SJ6304) in 1910 & 1915.

In 1975 Henry Hand found it in a corn field at Alcaston (SO4587), and it was still there in 1986 (Mary Fuller) and 1990 (Helen Davidson). Pat Parker saw it on the edge of a field at Cantlop (SJ5105) in 1981, and Jane Ing recorded it in a newly-seeded grassland at Weston Lullingfields (SJ4125) in 1992. The only other record for the county is from waste ground at Eaton Constantine (SJ5908, Rob Stokes, 1996). It is on the edge of its range in Shropshire, and from these few records it seems to occur now only as a casual.

Arabis glabra L. (Bernh.)
Tower mustard
Archaeophyte. Extinct (1897).

This species occurs in ruderal habitats, mainly on roadsides, and seems to have been a casual in Shropshire. It requires disturbed, slightly calcareous, sandy soil. It is Nationally Scarce and is considered to be a priority species under the UK BAP, although its claim to nativity is not very strong.

Edward Williams recorded it on ditch banks at Badger (SO7699), Beckbury (SO7601), Berrington (SJ5307), Ryton (SJ7602), Stockton (SJ7716) and Worfield (SO7595) in about 1800. George Lloyd collected it at Neach Hill (SJ7906) in 1830 and Leighton found it on the road side at Leaton Knolls (SJ4716) in 1835. Apparently it was Mrs Bowman (the wife of J.E. Bowman) who collected it near Shrewsbury (possibly in the same place as Leighton) in 1841, and at about that time it was recorded by T.C. Eyton at Marton (SJ4323) and by T.W. Wilson at Shotton (SJ4922).

Griffith Griffiths recorded it at Cardington (SO5095) in about 1870 and William Phillips found it still at Leaton Knolls and Berrington in 1878. Some time before 1889 William Beckwith found it in the lane near Moreton Corbet (SJ5623) and William Beacall saw it at the Cliffe (SJ3920) and at Marton (SJ4323). William Painter recorded it in the parish of Ryton (ca. SJ7602) in 1894 and in 1897 John Fraser collected it at Claverley (SO7993). This is the last properly confirmed record for the county, but Sinker (1985) maps several other sites for it from Hamilton's Flora of 1913, and gives two unconfirmed

and slightly dubious records for Poles Coppice (SJ3904) and Snailbeach (SJ3702) that date from the 1970s (D. Daniels).

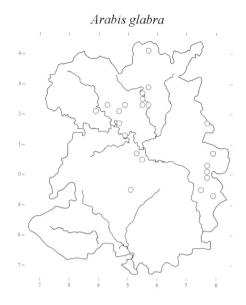

Arabis glabra

[*Astragalus danicus* Retz.]
Purple Milk-vetch
Not in Shropshire.

In 1864 there was apparently a report in the *Gardener's Chronicle* of this species at Quatford (SO7390). It seems quite possible, as the plant grows in calcareous grassland, which would have been present at Quatford, and it occurs not far away near the mouth of the Severn, but the record as it stands seems insufficient evidence on which to count this species a native of the county.

Astragalus glycyphyllos L.
Wild Liquorice
Native. Rare.

Sinker (1985) describes this as a plant of woodland edges, which makes a good case for it to be considered a native species, but it also occurs sometimes in disturbed habitats. Its distribution in Britain is mostly around the Midlands region, which is also suggestive of native status.

It was recorded by Williams in about 1800 'by the side of the turnpike road in the hollow way below Fox Farm' (SJ5209) and in a gravel pit at Round Hill (SJ4813) – neither of which sound much like woodland edge. Thomas Purton recorded it in 'Bucks orchard, Hoard's Park' (SO7194) in 1817 and Andrew Bloxam collected it on the banks of the Llangollen Canal at Ellesmere (SJ4034) in 1841. These both seem like ruderal habitats, too. In 1856 George Jorden listed it as a plant of the Wyre Forest (ca. SO7376), but that could have been in Worcestershire. In 1880 Beckwith discovered it on the High Rock, Bridgnorth (SO7293), where it has subsequently been seen by Stan Turner (1967), Winifred Hutton (1975 & 1985), and Joan Brown (1991).

Beckwith also recorded it at Rindleford Bridge (SO7395) and at Birch (SJ4033) in the 1890s. Diamond was the first to record it in the vicinity of Baschurch (SJ4221), which could have been a reference to The Berth (SJ4223), where William Phillips found it in 1892, and it was subsequently seen by Pat Parker in 1983 and 1991. Parker also found it in a green lane at Stanwardine in the Fields (SJ4124) in 1982 and 1991.

There are two other recent records for the county: Paul Bell recorded it at Hawkstone Park (SJ5729) in 1987, and John Clayfield discovered a small population at Dudmaston (SO7491) in 2000.

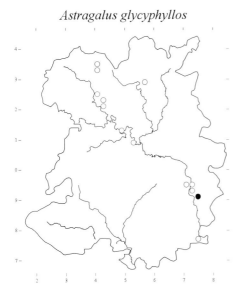

Astragalus glycyphyllos

Astrantia major L.

Astrantia

Neophyte. Rare.

Astrantia was famously found at Stoke Wood (SO4280) by Arthur Aikin in 1824 – the first British record. It has subsequently been recorded there many times, most recently by Audrey Ashwell in 1992. It appears well naturalised here and in Beechfield Dingle (SJ3005), where it was first recorded by Reg Harrison & Llewelyn Lloyd in 1954, and was most recently recorded by Dave Buckingham in 2000. It is not generally considered a native species, but whether it was introduced by the Romans or more recently is a matter of debate. It is also recorded as an obvious garden escape at a few other localities in the county, and is now widely established throughout Britain.

Baldellia ranunculoides (L.) Parl.

Lesser Water-plantain

Native. Extinct (1996).

This is one of the most rapidly declining species in Britain, having disappeared from most of its range in the lowlands over the last century or so. In the New Atlas C.D. Preston attributes the loss to the cessation of grazing around shallow water bodies. In Shropshire it used to occur around most of the meres. In about 1800 Edward Williams found it at Berrington Pool (SJ5207), Betton Pool (SJ5107), Bomere Pool (SJ4908), Hencott Pool (SJ4916), and in ditches at Hordley (SJ3830) and Newport (SJ7419). Leighton (1841) saw it again at Berrington Pool and Hencott Pool, and lists records for Cole Mere (SJ4333, A. Bloxam), Haughmond Hill (SJ5414, Leighton), Kynnersley (SJ6716, R.G. Higgins), Lilleshall (SJ7315, R.G. Higgins), Shawbury Heath (SJ5420, E. Elsmere) and The Mere at Ellesmere (SJ4034, A. Bloxam & F. Dickinson).

R. Anslow listed it as a species of the Weald Moors (ca. SJ6717) in 1865, and in the 1880s William Beckwith found it at Berrington Pool, The Mere, and White Mere (SJ4132). The last record for Berrington Pool was in 1907, when Miss H.M. Auden reported it there. The same year J. Ramsbottom found it at Brown Moss (SJ5639), which is the only site it has been seen at since. There are records by Miss H.M. Bigwood (1956), Sinker (1961), Keith Bell (1975), Walker (1985, 1993), Trueman (1987, 1992, 1996), Perring (1993), Jean Hooson (1994) and Sarah Whild (1995, 1996). Brown Moss is now ungrazed and overgrown, and the *Baldellia*, like many other rare species, has gone from there.

A record for Wildmoor Pool (SO4296) by NCC surveyors in 1983 was probably an error.

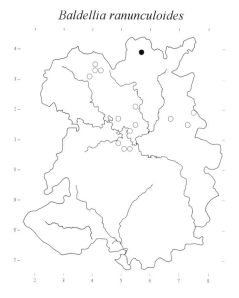

Baldellia ranunculoides

Bidens cernua L. var. *radiata* DC.
Nodding Bur-marigold
Native. Rare.

Although Nodding Bur-marigold (*Bidens cernua*) is not rare (it is found throughout the north of the county), the form with large ray florets is far less common. It was found at Brown Moss (SJ5639) by Edward Rutter in 1956 and still flourishes there (Whild, 2001). A second site, at Hickory Hollow near Whitchurch (SJ5341) was discovered by Rosa Ford in 1998 and a third locality near Edgerley (SJ3418) was found by Kate Thorne in 2003.

Blysmus compressus (L.) Panz. Ex Link
Flat-sedge
Native. Extinct (1886).

This is a rare and declining species of calcareous fens and old meadows, mostly now restricted to northern England. In Shropshire it used to occur at the base of the Wenlock Edge (SO5696), where it was found by Edward Williams in about 1800, and subsequently seen by Robert Serjeantson in 1878 and William Beacall in 1886.

Bolboschoenus maritimus (L.) Palla
Sea Club-rush
Neophyte. Rare.

This is a common plant of salt marshes and muddy places near the coast throughout most of the British Isles except the very north of Scotland. It was recorded by W.E. Beckwith at Hawkstone Park (SJ5730) in 1882, and it was still there in 1951 (R.C. Palmer). Charles Sinker found it in a pond at Preston Montford (SJ4314) in 1957 and it is still there (K. Hayward, 2001). It was probably introduced deliberately or accidentally at both sites.

Brachypodium pinnatum (L.) P. Beauv.
Tor-grass
Neophyte. Rare.

This species of calcareous grassland is often considered an invasive weed in the south and east of England, but Shropshire is somewhat beyond its range and it occurs here only as a casual. It has been recorded along a railway line at Albrighton (SJ8005, Brendan Carleton & Owen Mountford, 1979); on a roadside in Coalbrookdale (SJ6705, Godfrey Blunt conf. I.C. Trueman & P.M. Benoit, 1983) and on an old spoil heap at Clee Hill (SO6074, John Bingham, 1990).

Bromopsis benekenii (Lange) Holub
Lesser Hairy-brome
Native. Rare.

The distribution of Lesser Hairy-brome in Britain is rather curious. It occurs in calcareous woodlands, thinly scattered throughout Britain. In Shropshire it was recorded by Augustin Ley and William Moyle Rogers on Wenlock Edge in 1909, and subsequently by C.A. Sinker in Harton Hollow (SO4887) in 1963 and again by Sarah Whild (conf. Stace) in 2001.

[*Bromus commutatus* Schrader]
Meadow Brome
Not in Shropshire.

This species is common in the south-east of Britain, but it seems to stop abruptly at about the Shropshire border. There are no confirmed records for the county, and it is considered by Stace (1997) to be possibly just a subspecies of *B. racemosus*, so voucher specimens really are essential.

The existing field records are as follows: Hadnall (SJ5220), William Phillips, 1878; Sutton Maddock (SJ7201), William Painter, 1894; Hopesay (SO3884), T.E. Mitchell, 1977; Wentnor (SO3794), Joyce Warren, 1978; Priest Weston (SO2896), Joyce Roper, 1982; Oreton (SO6580), I.C. Trueman, 1994; Market Drayton (SO6735), Trueman, 1995. It would be interesting to have confirmation of any of these records.

Bromus racemosus L.
Smooth Brome
Archaeophyte. Rare.

This is a grass of damp, unimproved meadows that has never been common in Shropshire. In Leighton's Flora it is listed in just two sites: Hadnall (SJ5220, Elsmere) and Coalbrookdale (SJ6604, Dickinson). There was a record in Hamilton's Flora of 1913 for it at Benthall Edge (SJ6503). G.H. Griffiths recorded it at All Stretton (SO4695) in 1870, but all his records must be treated with caution. Another unconfirmed record for it was at Morton Pool (SJ3024) in 1981, by Peter Welsh & Chris Walker.

It was found by Sarah Whild to be locally abundant in a meadow on Shropshire Wildlife Trust's Melverley Farm (SJ5840) in 1998. It has subsequently been collected in a field at Astley Abbots (SO7096) by Mark Lawley in 1999; at Lower Broughton (SO3190) by Dave Buckingham in 2000; and at Berrington Pool (SJ5207) by Whild. All

four recent records were confirmed by L.M. Spalton.

Bromus secalinus L.
Rye Brome
Archaeophyte. Extinct (1904).

This species is considered to be an introduction that formerly survived as an agricultural weed. It was recorded by Williams in a field at Berrington (SJ5206) in 1797 was also listed in Leighton's Flora at Hadnall (SJ5220, Elsmere), Oakly Park (SO4876, Spare), Stanwardine (SJ4024, Bowman), and Sharpstone Hill (SJ4909, Leighton). In 1904 Augustin Ley found it as a cornfield casual on Wenlock Edge, and it has not been recorded since.

Calamagrostis canescens (Wigg.) Roth
Purple Small-reed
Native. Scarce.

This species is mostly restricted to the meres in Shropshire, where sometimes it is quite abundant in W5 *Alnus glutinosa* woodland. It has been recorded at the following sites: Alkmund Park Pool (SJ4716, Wigginton, 1979), Betton Pool (SJ5107, Wigginton, 1979), Birchgrove Pool (SJ4323, Wigginton, 1979), Blake Mere (SJ5542, J.M. Hooson, 1993), Bomere Pool (SJ4908, Newbold & Walker, 1985), Cole Mere (SJ4333, J.E. Bowman, 1841), Crose Mere (SJ4230, Bowman, 1841; Wigginton, 1979; Whild & Lockton, 2003), Fenemere (SJ4422, Rose, 1959, and many recorders since, most recently Lockton 2003), Hencott Pool (SJ4916, Williams, 1800 and many since, most recently Lockton, 2003), Marton Pool, Baschurch (SJ4423, Williams, 1800; C. Fuller & P. Richards, 1968), Marton Pool, Chirbury (SJ2902, Wigginton, 1979), Morton Pool (SJ3023, Tattersfield, 1991; Lockton, 2003), Oss Mere (SJ5643, Skelding, 1951; Wigginton, 1979; A. Hillman & C. Walker, 1991), Shomere Pool (SJ5008, Lockton, 2003), and Sweat Mere (SJ4330, Sinker, 1958; Wigginton, 1979; W. Fojt, B. Wheeler & S. Shaw, 1986; Lockton, 2003).

It has been recorded in four sites that are not meres. Williams had it on ditch banks about

Battlefield (SJ5116) and Sundorne (SJ5215) in about 1800. It was first recorded in the Old River Bed in Shrewsbury (SJ4915) in 1963 (J.M. Way, ABRN), and subsequently by Chris Walker in 1979, Adrian Bayley & Dave Smallshire in 1983, Gill Castle in 1992, Sarah Whild in 1995, and Jane Ing in 2002. Castle also found it in an area of wet woodland in Telford (SJ6905) in 1998 (det. Whild).

Calamagrostis canescens

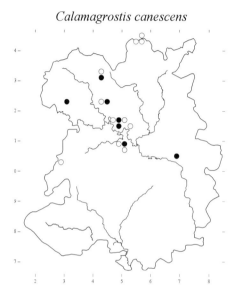

Calamagrostis epigejos (L.) Roth
Wood Small-reed
Native. Scarce.

Although it is common in the east of England, this species reaches the western edge of its range in Shropshire, and it has always been quite rare here. It was first recorded by Edward Elsmere (conf. Leighton) in about 1841 at Battlefield Church (SJ5117), where it has since been seen by Sinker (1965), J.M. Baker (1986), N. Anderson (1991), Whild & Lockton (1994), and Ing (2001). It grows on the edge of what are thought to be mediæval fishponds behind the churchyard.

Griffith Griffiths recorded it 'near Strefford' (SO4485) in about 1870, and it has since been recorded at nearby Marshbrook (SO4487) by Henry Hand (1977-1997). The record by Richard Benson and W. Yelland for Marton Pool, Chirbury (SJ2902) in 1899 is surely an error for *C. canescens*.

Bryan Fowler recorded it on the side of a stream near Spring Coppice (SJ8307) and by a field pond near Boscobel (SJ8406) in 1976 but it has not been seen in either of those sites again, despite searches.

Pat Parker and Jane Ing first recorded it on Haughmond Hill (SJ5413) in 1987, where it was later seen by Sarah Whild in 1993. Ian Trueman and other members of the Botanical Society discovered it at nearby Haughmond Abbey Woods (SJ5415) in 1995, and it has since been seen there by Whild (1997) and at Colin's Rough (SJ5316, Whild & Lockton, 2000 & 2004). Mags Cousins found an entirely new site at Snowdon Pool (SJ7801) in 2002.

Calamagrostis epigejos

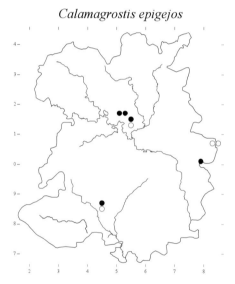

Callitriche hermaphroditica L.
Annual Water-starwort
Native. Rare.

The water-starworts are a difficult group to identify, and all unconfirmed field records must be treated with some caution. *C. hermaphroditica* is a northern species and an indicator of good water quality in mesotrophic lakes and pools. It is probably rare in Shropshire, although it seems to be somewhat over-recorded.

The first record was by Leighton, who collected it in a pit near Sharpstones Hill (SJ4909) some time in the 19th century (det. R.D. Meikle, K).

Rare Plants of Shropshire

Sinker found it in Cole Mere (SJ4333) in 1958, and it has subsequently been seen there by Wigginton (1979), Walker (1990), Lansdown (1997) and Whild (2003). Sinker also found it in the Llangollen Canal at Blake Mere (SJ4233, 1958) and in the Prees Branch Canal (SJ4934) in 1966, but it has not been seen in either of those sites again. It still occurs in the Montgomery Canal in Wales, but the only recent records for the Shropshire length (SJ3326, C. Newbold, 2001) are considered to be unconfirmed.

Frank Perring found it at White Mere (SJ4132) in 1975, where it has since been seen by Wigginton (1979), Walker (1987-1992) and Perring again (1993). Walker added Marton Pool, Chirbury (SJ2902) to the site list in 1988. In 1990 Pat Parker and Jane Ing found it in Walford Pool (SJ4320), where it had apparently been introduced with other rare water plants, and where it persisted until 1991.

Callitriche hermaphroditica

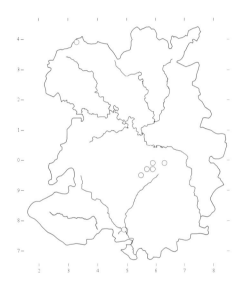

Campanula glomerata L.
Clustered Bellflower
Native. Extinct (1935).

The only really reliable records of this species in Shropshire are from the Wenlock Edge, where it has been recorded by Williams at Lutwyche (SO5594) in about 1800; by William Penny Brookes at Hilltop (SO5696) and Much Wenlock (SO6299) in 1841; by Dickinson at Lutwyche again in

1841; by Beckwith at Presthope (SO5897) in 1882 and again by George Potts in 1903, 1925 and 1933. There are two records that do not fit: Mary McGhee recorded it on the banks of the River Corve at Bromfield (SO4876) in 1841, and Ellen Lloyd found it in Coed-yr-Allt Wood (SJ2339) in 1935. If those two records are correct, they would probably have been of casuals or garden escapes. The reasons for its decline in Shropshire are not obvious.

Campanula glomerata

Campanula patula L.
Spreading Bellflower
Native. Scarce.

The natural habitat of this plant is woodland edge alongside rivers. It is also found on hedgebanks along quiet lanes. It is Nationally Scarce and declining in Britain, with just 37 dots in the New Atlas. In Britain it is almost entirely restricted to the catchment of the River Severn.

It was once quite common in south Shropshire, along the valleys of the Severn, Clun, Corve, Teme and Onny, but it is now reduced to just four sites, at Wentnor (SO39W, Sylvia Kingsbury, 1998), Llanfair Waterdine (SO2277, Dorothy Young, 2003), Pentre Hodre (SO3276, Clayfield & Whild, 2004) and Bedstone (SO3775, Clayfield, 1998).

Edward Williams, in about 1800, described it as common and recorded it on ditch-banks about Berrington (SJ5206), Cound (SJ5505), Eaton Mascott (SJ5305), Montford (SJ4114) and Shipton (SO5691). Joseph Babington considered it to be very common around Ludlow (SO5174) and at Caynham Camp (SO5473) in 1803.

In Turner & Dillwyn's Botanical Guide (1805) it is listed for Shelton bank (SJ4613), Montford Bridge bank (SJ4315), Pitchford (SJ5303), Condover (SJ4906), Leaton Shelf (SJ4718) and Caynham Camp again. Henry Bidwell collected it at Rudge (SO8197) in 1825. Leighton (1841) gives many of the above, plus new records for Acton Burnell (SJ5302, Corbett), Acton Scott (SO4589, Corbett), Astley (SJ5217, Leighton), Berrington (SJ5206, Corbett), Berrington Pool (SJ5207, Leighton), Bickley Coppice (SJ4416, Leighton), Brockton (SJ7203, Dickinson), Condover (SJ4906, Corbett), Cound (SJ5505, Lloyd), Frodesley (SJ5101, Corbett), High Rock, Bridgnorth (SO7293, Crotch), Larden (SO5693, Brookes), Munslow (SO5287, Dickinson), Oakly Park (SO4876, Spare), Pitchford (SJ5303, Corbett), Wellington (SJ6511, Edwin Lees), and along Watling Street (Lees).

There is little evidence for a decline until well into the 20th century. In 1849 the Reverend Sandford recorded it at Whitchurch (SJ5441) and in 1856 George Jorden listed it for the Wyre Forest (SO77). William Beckwith found it to be still frequent about Berrington and Cound in the 1880s. Its known range was extended to the south-west of the county in 1892, when William Phillips recorded it at Prolley Moor (SO3993) and Bedstone (SO3675). In 1903 J.A. Panter found it at Bettws-y-crwyn (SO2081); in 1904 W.E. Thompson found it on Ragleth Hill (SO4572); and in 1905 H.H. Hughes had it near Clun (SO3080).

Hamilton's Flora of 1913 added five new sites, at SJ40G & Z, SJ41B, SJ50P & SO27W, but the details are unknown. In 1922 G.M. Furley found it by the Severn at Ford (SJ4114) and near Wentnor (SO3892). The Whites, Mr A.E. and Miss K., found it at Wroxeter (SJ5608) and in the old site at Montford Bridge (SJ4315) in 1923. In 1939 a visitor from London, Laurence Payne, recorded it as common between Cheney Longville and Wistanstow (SO4284). By this time it was disappearing from the middle reaches of the county where it had once been so common. Honor Pendlebury found it at Little Stretton (SO4491) in 1953 and Stan Turner reported it on the river cliff at Preston Montford (SJ4314) in 1972, where it was apparently known to Charles Sinker and Philip Oswald, but since then it has been restricted to the south-west of the county.

Other recent sites include Myndmill (SO3888, Ian Bonner, 1971), Knighton (SO2575, Joyce Roper, 1977) and Pentre Hodre (SO3276, Roper, 1978), Stowe (SO3072, Rob Rowe, 1979), Llanwolley (SO2277, Will Prestwood, 1980) and Hidmore (SO2178, Roper, 1980).

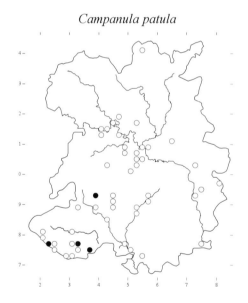

Campanula patula

Cardamine bulbifera (L.) Crantz
Coralroot
Neophyte. Rare.

This woodland plant has a single population in Shropshire in the grounds of Broncroft Castle (SO5486), where it was recorded by Mary Fuller in 1978 and 1992. It is presumably an introduction, but the Shropshire plants are apparently of the native variety, which is sometimes grown in cultivation.

Cardamine impatiens L.
Narrow-leaved Bittercress
Native. Extinct (1959).

This is a plant of base-rich woodlands, particularly coppiced ones, as it benefits from the disturbance. It is likely to be found in W8 *Fraxinus excelsior-Acer campestre-Mercurialis perennis* woodland, especially in limestone areas. It requires high light levels, base-rich, fertile soil and moderate moisture levels. It was included as a 'B' species in Sinker's *Flora*, so none of the records made in the 1970s and early '80s have a precise location, recorder or even date. This is unfortunate, as it has not been seen since then, and we have to go back to 1959 for the last reliable record for the county.

The first record was by Littleton Brown at Bishops Castle (SO3288) in about 1725. Edward Williams found it at Little Wenlock (SJ6408) in about 1800. In Leighton's Flora there are also records for Tinker's Hill (SO5272, Andrew Bloxam), Church Stretton (SO4593, Thomas Bodenham), Clee Hill (SO6077, Mary McGhie) and Shelderton Rock (SO4177, Thomas Salwey).

R.M. Serjeantson recorded it near Caer Caradoc (SO4795) in 1880 and Beckwith found it to be plentiful at 'Helmeth, and woods above Watling Street between Church and Little Stretton' (SO4693) in 1889. Spencer Bickham, Augustin Ley and W. Moyle Rogers found it on nearby Hope Bowdler (SO4792) in 1909. On the Long Mynd, J.W. Heath recorded it in The Batch (SO4495) in 1900 and, with William Beacall, in Ashes Hollow (SO4293) in 1904. J.B. Duncan found it near the colliery siding at Highley (SO7484) in 1903 and Miss H.M. Auden recorded it near Condover (SJ4906) in 1907. The Reverend O.M. Feilden saw it in 1920 at Hardwick (SJ3734). The last detailed record for the county was by Mrs Paish and Edward Rutter at Tantree Bank (SJ2906), where eight plants were seen in ancient semi-natural woodland.

The Flora Project records do seem to be in roughly the same areas as the previous ones, but it is unsatisfactory to not have the details. They should be considered slightly dubious. It is apparent that *C. impatiens* has never been common in the county. Leighton described it as rare. It should be looked for in areas of base-rich rock outcrops in woodland, or along tracks and roadsides after trees have been coppiced or felled: the areas around Church Stretton seem the most promising. A recent record for Marrington Dingle could not be substantiated.

In the New Atlas there are just 75 current dots for this species, so it remains firmly in the Nationally Scarce category. Its distribution is centred around the Welsh Marches and the Seven valley, so Shropshire remains well within its range.

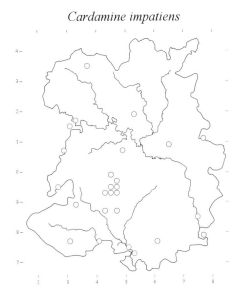

Cardamine impatiens

Carduus tenuiflorus Curtis
Slender Thistle
Neophyte. Rare.

This is a predominantly coastal species in Britain with only a scattered distribution inland. It was recorded by Edward Williams on ditch-banks around the old limestone quarry near Harnage (SJ5604) in about 1800, where it was rediscovered by Pat Parker in 1975 (SJ5604), but has not been seen since. Doris Pugh found it in a lay-by along the A5 at Queen's Head (SJ3326) in 1968 (conf. P.M. Benoit) and Rob Stokes reported it from the nearby Knockin Heath (SJ3521) in 1994. The only other record for it in the county is by the Whitchurch Canal (probably ca. SJ5341) by Jean Hooson in 1993.

Carex acuta L.
Slender Tufted-sedge
Native. Scarce.

In Shropshire, this species seems to occur only along the banks of the Severn (and formerly the Tern), and very occasionally in ditches and wet meadows within the flood plain. Other records, given in Sinker's Flora and elsewhere, are unsubstantiated. It is probably not rare in the county but, owing to the difficulty in recording it along the steep banks of the river, there are few records.

Edward Williams recorded it by the Tern (SJ5510) in about 1800, where William Beckwith also saw it is 1882. Other records in Leighton's Flora of 1841 seem dubious: Francis Dickinson listed it for the Malthouse Pool in Coalbrookdale (SJ6604) and Leighton himself found it at Alkmund Park Pool (SJ4716), which Phillips later cited (probably in error) as Haughmond Park Pool in 1878.

A specimen collected by Beckwith in 1884 was identified only after his death in 1889, by Dr S.O.I. Almquist. Unfortunately the site is not known, but Beckwith did write in 1882 that it is occasionally found by the Severn, so that is probably the site. W.P. Hamilton also found it by the Severn at Underdale (SJ5013) in 1896.

A record for Moon Pool, Benthall (SJ6602), was made by W.H. Painter in 1901 (det. F.W. White), and he also found it by the Severn at Coalport (SJ7002) the same year. Frank Perring recorded it at Attingham Park (SJ5510) in 1972; with Ian Bonner in the Severn at Atcham (SJ5309) in 1975; and in the Severn at Dowles (SO7776) in 1976. Sarah Stafford extended its known range upstream to Loton Park (SJ3516) in 1979, and Bill Thompson found it in several places near Hampton Loade (SO7486) in 1980. Trueman recorded it at Buildwas (SJ6304) and Leighton (SJ6004) in 1981.

In 1995 Dan Wrench and Steve Ayliffe boated along the Severn looking for this species, and recorded it at Atcham (SJ5309) and Shrewsbury (SJ4812 & SJ5013). Rob Stokes discovered it by the Severn at Cronkhill (SJ5308) in 1995. One small patch used to occur by the Severn near Porthill

Bridge in Shrewsbury (Whild & Lockton 1997) but this area has become very shaded recently and it seems to have gone.

In 2003 Kate Thorne found it in two new places in the flood plain of the Severn near Melverley (SJ3319 & SJ3418), together with its hybrid with *Carex nigra* (see *C. ˣelytroides*).

Carex acuta

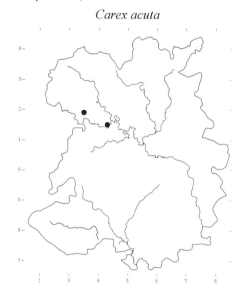

Carex ˣboenninghauseniana Weihe
(*Carex paniculata × remota*)
Native. Rare.

This hybrid sedge is quite distinctive, as its tussocks are the size of those of *C. paniculata* but the flowering spikes are like those of *C. remota*. It has been recorded only twice in the county. In 1973 Charles Sinker found it by the Prees Branch Canal (SJ4933) and in 2003 Peter Lukey collected it at Trefonen Marshes (SJ2426, conf. M.S. Porter).

Carex diandra Schrank
Lesser Tussock-sedge
Native. Extinct (1956).

At one time this species seems to have been quite widely distributed in Shropshire, although no voucher specimens are known. It is interesting to note that Leighton's description and drawing of '*C. teretiuscula*' show the utricle to be broadly winged, which is a characteristic of *C. paniculata*, not *diandra*, so there must be some doubt about the early records.

If it was indeed *C. diandra*, Edward Williams recorded it at Cole Mere (SJ4333), Hencott Pool (SJ4816), Shomere Pool (SJ5007), and on a ditch in the Weald Moors, between Adeney and Buttery (SJ6917) in about 1800. In 1834 C.C. Babington and W.A. Leighton found it at Bomere Pool (SJ4908). Also listed in Leighton's 1841 Flora are additional records for Cole Mere by J.E. Bowman and W.A. Leighton, one for 'near Oswestry' (ca. SJ2929) by T. Salwey, and one for The Mere at Ellesmere (SJ4034) by Bowman. In 1882 W.E. Beckwith described it as plentiful at the lower end of Colemere Mere.

Carex diandra

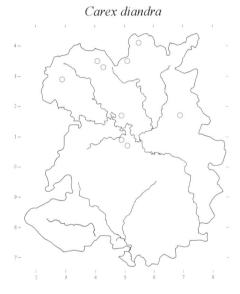

A record for Whitchurch (SJ5441) given in Sinker's Flora is presumably from Hamilton's missing Flora of 1913. The only other records for the county date from 1956, when Allan McGregor Stirling recorded it at The Mere, Ellesmere (SJ4034) and at Whixall (SJ53). Again, there are no voucher specimens. It is a plant of peaty soils that is shown in the New Atlas to have declined almost to extinction throughout England and Wales, with many of the losses being a century ago or more. Thus, the records for Shropshire are entirely possible, but it would be very reassuring to find some herbarium specimens.

Carex digitata L.
Fingered Sedge
Native. Rare.

With just 24 dots in the New Atlas, this is one of Britain's rarer sedges, occurring in limestone woodlands from the lower Severn valley northwards to Yorkshire and Cumbria. The only known location for it in Shropshire is at Tick Wood (SJ6302), where it was discovered by Chris Walker in 1977, and is still present. In a good year there can be about 100 clumps present, but in 2003 fewer than a dozen were seen by Sarah Whild. Tick Wood is an ancient W8 *Fraxinus excelsior-Acer campestre-Mercurialis perennis* woodland, but it is privately owned and access is restricted. It is one of the few sites in Shropshire that was considered Grade 1 in the Nature Conservation Review (Ratcliffe 1977).

Carex distans L.
Distant Sedge
Native. Extinct (ca. 1892).

This is a mainly coastal species that sometimes occurs in damp grasslands inland. Williams recorded it at Eaton Mascott (SJ5305), Golding (SJ5403), Pitchford (SJ5303), Shawbury Heath (SJ5420) and 'under the Wrekin' (SJ6308). These are all unconfirmed field records, but they are widely accepted (see Sinker *et al.* 1985 p. 302). Unfortunately the whereabouts of any voucher specimen is unknown, so it is not possible to confirm them. Beckwith apparently collected a specimen some time in the 19th century at Eaton Constantine (SJ5906), which is confirmed by Max Walters (SHY).

Carex divulsa Stokes
Grey Sedge
Native. Rare.

Although this is a common species in the south of England and Ireland, Shropshire is just on the edge of its range, and it seems to occur here only as a casual. Of the two subspecies, the only one to have been found in Shropshire is ssp. *divulsa*. It has been recorded on roadsides, ditch-banks, and along paths in gardens. The first record was by Leighton (conf. R.W. David, BM) at Cloud Coppice (SJ5306) in 1840. Phillips listed it as still there in 1878. Beckwith found it at Cressage (SJ5904) and at Pitchford Hall (SJ5204) in 1882. In Diamond's Fl. Oswestry (1891) it is listed as having been recorded at Llynclys (SJ2824) by the Oswestry & Welshpool Naturalists. A record for Llanyblodwel (SJ2322) by Isaac Watkin in 1900 is considered unconfirmed, as is Will Prestwood's 1980 record for Brownheath (SJ4529).

The first recent record was by Mary Fuller in 1974 at her own house in Aston Munslow (SO5186), where it could be considered an introduction – but the same could be said of all the Shropshire plants. It was still there in 1998 (Fuller & Whild). Dick David recorded it at Dowles (SO7776) in 1975: this site is in modern Worcestershire but v.c. 40. In 1977 Ellen Heywood-Waddington recorded its brief appearance on a roadside at Neen Savage (SO6777), and in 1979 Malcolm Clark and John Bingham found it by the side of the Dowles Brook in Chamberline Wood (SO7676), where it still occurred in 1986 (Bingham). Pat Parker recorded it at Stevenshill (SJ5603) in 1980; Rob Stokes found it in Badger Dingle (SO7699) in 1997; and Sarah Whild discovered a few patches in Dudmaston Dingle (SO7488) in 2003.

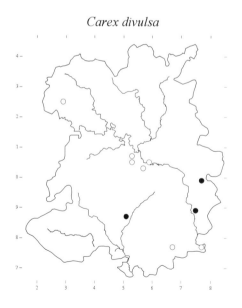

Carex divulsa

Carex elongata L.
Elongated Sedge
Native. Scarce.

Why *Carex elongata* is so rare nationally is not well understood. It occurs in wet woodland throughout Britain and Ireland, but with a very localised distribution. In Shropshire it occurs at several of the meres, notably Cole Mere (SJ4333), where it was discovered in 1840 by J.E. Bowman; Hencott Pool (SJ4916, Wigginton, 1979); Sweat Mere (SJ4330, Wigginton, 1979); and White Mere (SJ4132, Beckwith, 1880). It also used to occur at The Mere, Ellesmere (SJ4034), where it was discovered by Andrew Bloxam in 1850 and was last seen by Wigginton in 1980. A record for Bomere Pool (SJ4908, Newbold, 1985) is unconfirmed. In addition to the sites at the meres, it was also known along the Llangollen Canal in two places (Fenns Bank, SJ5137, A. McG. Stirling 1956; and Colemere Bridge, SJ4333, R.W. David 1968). The explanation for this curious contrast in habitats seems to be that it grows on rotting wood, whether in woodland on the edge of a pool or on the decaying posts of a disused canal. Following the restoration of the Llangollen, it has disappeared from the latter habitat. Whether the wood serves merely as a convenient substrate or is more significant in the germination and establishment phase is not known.

Paul Bell recorded it at Betton Moss (SJ6836) in 1978, but reported that the site was destroyed in 1986 and Ian Trueman found it in what are thought to be the remains of mediæval fishponds at Haughmond Abbey (SJ5415) in 1988. J.D. Gray collected plants at Criftins (SJ3636) in 1893, but no-one has recorded it there since.

This species should be considered one of Shropshire's most important plants, ecologically. Its population sizes seem to fluctuate enormously, depending on the degree of inundation and state of decay of the carr woodland (or canal bank) in which it grows. The native habitat is W5 *Alnus glutinosa-Carex paniculata* woodland, although it is known to persist in eutrophic W6 *A. glutinosa-Urtica dioica* woodland at Hencott Pool.

It is currently known in just five or perhaps six sites in the county: Brownheath Moss, where it was abundant in 2003 (Lockton); Cole Mere, where there were about 50 clumps in 2004 (Lockton); Haughmond Abbey, where there were about two dozen clumps in 2004 (Lockton), Hencott Pool, where the population seems to have crashed to just a few clumps (Lockton 2003); Sweat Mere, where it is still abundant (Lockton 2003); and White Mere, where it was last recorded by Chris Walker in 1990.

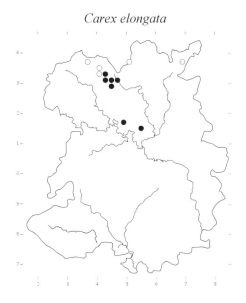

Carex elongata

Carex ^x*elytroides* Fries

(Carex acuta × nigra)
Native. Rare.

Kate Thorne first discovered this hybrid sedge in a field near Edgerley (SJ3418) in 2001 (conf. A.C. Jermy), and then found a second population near Ford (SJ4214) in 2002 (conf. A.C. Jermy). It grows with both parents in wet meadows close to the Severn.

Carex ^x*involuta*

(Carex rostrata × vesicaria)
Native. Extinct (1959).

Charles Sinker recorded this hybrid at Black Marsh (SO3299) in 1958 and at Brown Moss (SJ5639) in 1959, but it has not been seen in the county since then.

Carex lasiocarpa Ehrh.
Slender Sedge
Native. Rare.

Growing in standing water in fen or mire vegetation, this plant requires low levels of nutrients and no shade. It has declined dramatically throughout lowland England but remains common in western Scotland and Ireland. In Shropshire it has been recorded at the following sites: Berrington Moss (SJ5206, Sinker, 1965; Walker 1975 & 1984), Berrington Pool (SJ5207, Leighton, 1836; Beckwith, 1880; Sinker, 1965; Wigginton 1979; Walker & Whild 1996), Betton Pool (SJ5107, Dickinson, 1841), Blake Mere (SJ4133, Bowman, 1841), Bomere Pool (Leighton, 1841; Beckwith, 1882; Melvill, 1906), Cole Mere (SJ4233, Bowman & Leighton, 1841; Beckwith, 1880), Lin Can Moss (SJ3721, Walker, 1981; Bayley & Smallshire 1983), Shomere (SJ5007, Williams 1800), The Mere, Ellesmere (SJ4034, Williams, 1800), Wem Moss (SJ4734, Sinker, 1960 & 1962), and White Mere (SJ4132, Williams, 1800). The only site it has been recorded in that is not one of the meres & mosses is by the side of the disused railway near Ellesmere, SJ4236, where Keith Bell recorded it in 1976.

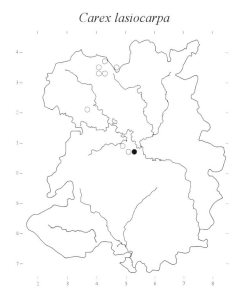

Carex lasiocarpa

There are just two sites at which it has been recorded recently. At Berrington Pool it occurs very sparsely around the western and northern sides of the pool amongst stands of *Carex rostrata* (Whild & Lockton, 2003). It is also still present at nearby Berrington Moss (Iain Diack, 2004).

Carex limosa L.
Bog-sedge
Native. Extinct (1976).

As its name suggests, bog sedge occurs primarily in lowland peat bogs, mainly in the west of Scotland and Ireland. In Shropshire it is a glacial relic which persisted into recent times in four sites. Williams found two of these in about 1800: Weeping Cross Bog (SJ5110) and 'Lee,' which was part of a great expanse of mire south of The Mere at Ellesmere (SJ4032), in about 1800. Babington and Leighton found it at Bomere Pool (SJ4908) in 1834, and Beckwith found the fourth – Clarepool Moss (SJ4334) in 1882. Diamond's 1891 record for Llynclys (SJ2824) and Watkins's 1900 record for Llanyblodwel (SJ2322) are both dubious. There were no records for it in the 20th century until it was rediscovered at Clarepool Moss by Francis Rose and David Bellamy in 1959. The last confirmed record for it there was by Keith Bell in 1976, in a small bog 150m south-west of the pool. This site is now dense birch woodland, and it is almost certainly gone from there.

Carex montana L.
Soft-leaved Sedge
Native. Scarce.

This was first discovered in the county in the Wyre Forest (ca. SO7476) by J.B. Duncan in 1901, but a specimen collected in 1876 by J.H. Thompson at Cooper's Mill (SO7576) was later identified by W.H. Painter. It has since been recorded many times in the Wyre Forest, notably by M.E. Smith in 1972, R.W. David in 1975 and 1977, and M.C. Clark and C. Fuller in 1976. John Bingham took on the challenge of plotting its distribution within the Forest in 1986, and he discovered a new population at Catherton Common (SO6177) in 1999, extending its known range 8 km to the west.

In the Wyre Forest it grows at Breakneck Bank (SO7076), Chamberline Wood (SO7676), Longdon Orchard (SO7477), Longdon Wood (SO7576) and Wimperhill Wood (SO7476). It often grows on steep banks in oak wood (often *Quercus* [x]*rosacea* in the Wyre), probably in W10 *Quercus robur-Pteridium aquilinum-Rubus fruticosus* woodland. We have no detailed information about its ecology, but anecdotal comments suggest that it benefits from occasional coppicing. In Catherton Common it occurs in rough grassland.

In the New Atlas *C. montana* is shown as occurring in 38 hectads – considerably more than in the 1962 Atlas, but still firmly within the Nationally Scarce category. The increase is due to better recording in its strongholds in the New Forest and in south Wales. A dot for SO78 in the New Atlas appears to be an error.

The sites for this species in Shropshire appear to be close to the northern limit of its distribution. With an Ellenberg value for fertility of just 1 (Hill *et al.* 1999), it is highly sensitive to pollution and disturbance and hence a good indicator of habitat quality. There is no obvious threat to it in the county and no evidence of any decline.

Carex muricata L. ssp. *muricata*
Scarce Prickly-sedge
Native. Rare.

Scarce Prickly-sedge is believed to be one of the rarest species in Britain. It is closely related to *Carex muricata* ssp. *lamprocarpa*, which is widespread and common on neutral to acidic soils, but this rare subspecies, which is restricted to limestone soils, and flowers earlier in the year, is known in just seven sites in the British Isles. It seems possible that it will eventually be promoted to a full species, as the two currently recognised subspecies have little ecological overlap. *Carex spicata* is the third member of this difficult group, and with a wider tolerance of soil types it can occur with either of the *muricata* subspecies.

In Shropshire *C. muricata* ssp. *muricata* was discovered by Sarah Whild in 1999 at Jones's

Rough (SJ2424), where it occurs in a patch of open limestone scree, occupying an area of approximately 10m × 10m, with about 500 plants in total. A second site on Moelydd, just a few hundred yards from the original one, was first reported by Chris Walker later the same year, although this was not confirmed until specimens were collected in June 2000 by Lockton & Whild. It turned out that there were 1,000 plants in fifteen discrete populations. The two sites so far discovered in Shropshire contain some 90% of the currently known British population of this species.

It is described by David & Kelcey (1985) as being common in northern Europe and Russia. In Shropshire it occurs in CG2d *Festuca ovina-Avenula pratensis* grassland, *Dicranum scoparium* subcommunity. For now the Shropshire populations seem to be secure and thriving.

Carex ^x*pseudoaxillaris* K. Richt.

Carex ^{x}*pseudoaxillaris* K. Richt.
(*Carex otrubae* × *remota*)
Native. Extinct (1901).

There is a report in the *Record of Bare Facts* for the year 1901 that there is a specimen of this hybrid collected at Llynclys Pool (SJ2824) in the herbarium of a certain Miss Lloyd. No further details are known. Also in 1901 the schoolteacher Edward Cleminshaw apparently collected it on the Leominster Canal (SO6670).

Carex viridula ssp. *brachyrrhyncha*
(Celak.) B. Schmid
Long-stalked Yellow-sedge
Native. Extinct (1989).

Of the three subspecies of yellow sedge, ssp. *oedocarpa* occurs in acid upland flushes and is common in Shropshire, ssp. *brachyr-rhyncha* occurs in lowland calcareous flushes and is rare, and ssp. *viridula* occurs on the margins of neutral pools, and is also rare.

Carex viridula ssp. *brachyrrhyncha* was first recorded in the county by Sinker at Crose Mere (SJ4430) in 1960. It has since been seen there by Keith Bell (1976), Martin Wigginton (1979), Chris Walker (1980) Ian Trueman

(1984) and Frank Perring (1989). It grew in the fen at the south-east end of the mere, which became very overgrown after it was fenced off for its own protection, and it has not been seen since then despite many searches. Records of this plant at Trefonen Marshes (SJ2426) are considered to be errors for *C. viridula* ssp. *oedocarpa*.

Carex viridula Michx. ssp. *viridula*
Small-fruited Yellow-sedge
Native. Extinct (1997).

This is a very westerly species in Britain, being common in the west of Scotland and around the coast. There it often grows in dune slacks and on the edges of salt marshes. Its only site in Shropshire was an example of an alternative habitat type – the bare margins of fluctuating fresh water bodies. It was discovered at Brown Moss (SJ5639) in 1963 by Charles Sinker, but was then thought to have gone extinct until it was refound by Trueman in 1985. It persisted until 1997 (Whild) until encroachment by willow scrub led to its demise through a combination of shading and changing the substrate through the deposition of leaf litter. This species is a component of the OV35 *Lythrum portula-Ranunculus flammula* community and is therefore an indicator of good habitat quality, with a requirement for low fertility and high light levels. There are hopes that it will return again following a programme of tree felling.

Centaurea cyanus L.
Cornflower
Archaeophyte. Rare.

Apparently this was never a very common plant in Shropshire, but it was almost eradicated in the 19th century by improved agricultural techniques. It now persists only at Pimhill Organic Farm (SJ4920, Buckingham, 2002), where it was first recorded by Rob Stokes & John Martin in 1993.

Joseph Babington considered it to be common in the vicinity of Ludlow (SO5174) in 1803, and Henry Spare recorded it at nearby Oakly Park (SO4876) in 1841. Joseph Baly saw it in field by the side of the road between Shrewsbury and Ludlow at about the same time. Leighton recorded it in field near Bomere Pool (SJ4908) and on Westfelton Moor (SJ3425) in 1841.

Griffith Griffiths considered it to be frequent in fields at Church Stretton (SO4593) in 1870, but although he accepted this record, it was not recorded as such by Richard Benson in 1904.

William Phillips, in 1878, repeated Leighton's record for Bomere, and added a record for a marsh near Berrington Station (SJ5206), which seems a curious habitat for it. William Beckwith gave rather more detailed records in 1880. He described it as occurring each year in the fields near Bomere Pool and at Eaton Mascott (SJ5305), and often in corn-fields in other places. Diamond (1891) said it occurred 'occasionally' around Oswestry (SJ2929).

In 1906 James Melvill found it at Meole Brace (SJ4810) and remarked that it was 'rather rare' in south Shropshire. In 1908 Miss H.M. Auden recorded it at Longden (SJ4508).

There is then a very long gap until the next record, and it seems likely that by this time it was only a casual, coming up from long-buried seed. J.B. Johnson found it in a field of oats at Lower Wood (SO4697) in 1944. It came up on waste ground by the roadside at Wilderhope (SO5392) in 1976 (K.M. Saville). In the same year Joan Connell recorded it in a field of stubble at The Isle, Bicton (SJ4616) and Bryan Fowler found it at Donington Church (SJ8004).

In 1977 Rachael Lees found it in a field margin at Meeson (SJ6620), and the following year she and Rachel Jefferson recorded it in a hay field at Child's Ercall (SJ6625). Mary Fuller discovered some plants in an old meadow at California (SO5280) in 1981.

It was quite abundant in a peaty field by the Roden at Wolverley (SJ4631, Lockton, 1995), but the grass was cut for silage before the cornflowers set seed. Plants found at Queen's Head (SJ3326, Whild & Lockton, 1996), Oilhouse Pasture (SJ6704, Thorne,

2003) and Lightmoor (SJ6606, G. Evans, 2004) were probably from sown seed.

Cornflower *Centaurea cyanus*

[*Cephalanthera damasonium* (Mill.) Druce]
White Helleborine
Not in Shropshire.

In 1940 Dr S.E. Chandler, a researcher from the Imperial Institute in London, recorded a few plants during what was probably a holiday in Shropshire. Among these was apparently a single specimen of *Cephalanthera damasonium* on Wenlock Edge, between Eaton and Westhope (ca. SO4888). This is significantly beyond the known range of the species and it seems quite likely to be an error for *C. longifolia*, or for an albino form of another orchid. In 1974 Mary Fuller claimed to have found it in two more locations along Wenlock Edge (SO6099 & SO5998) but could not find it again. Sinker did not accept those records for his Flora of 1985, and they should be regarded as dubious. To be fair, all three records are entirely possible, but without any sort of confirmation it seems best not to add this species to the county list.

Cephalanthera longifolia L.
Narrow-leaved Helleborine
Native. Extinct (1891).

In Leighton's Flora of 1841 Henry Bidwell recorded this species in a plantation near Ruckley (SJ7706) and Edwin Lees described it as occurring along rides in the Wyre Forest (SO77), although he doesn't specifically say that it was in Shropshire. A certain G.W. Turner is reputed to have recorded it near Ludlow (SO5175) in 1890, but we do not have any details. Finally, in 1891, J.D. LaTouche found it in a wood near Craven Arms (SO4382).

Cephalanthera longifolia

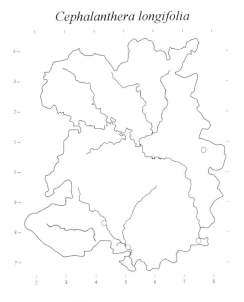

Cerastium diffusum Pers.
Sea Mouse-ear
Neophyte. Rare.

Although it is quite common around the coast, this species rarely occurs inland. It grows on dry, sandy soils and is sometimes found as a casual along railway lines and road sides. In Shropshire it was first recorded by Bryan Fowler in the goods yard at Albrighton railway station (SJ8204) in 1976. Doris Pugh and Peter Benoit found it on Llanymynech Hill (SJ2622) in 1977 (although this site is also claimed for Montgomeryshire). In 1991 Trueman found it in the quarries on Titterstone Clee (SO5975 & SO6076), where it has subsequently been seen by Whild (1996) and Thorne (1999).

Mark Lawley found it growing as a casual in Ludlow cattle market (SO5174) in 1999.

Chamaemelum nobile (L.) All.
Chamomile
Archaeophyte. Extinct (1961).

The old records of this species in Shropshire suggest that it was a plant of roadsides and commons, which would make it an archaeophyte. Edward Williams found it in about 1800 at Bayston Hill (SJ4808), Bicton Heath (SJ4513), by the finger post on Cound Moor (SJ5502), and by the side of the road between Lydbury and Bishop's Castle (SO3486). Leighton (1841) did not record it at all, but he reports that George Jorden considered it to be common at Oreton or, more likely perhaps, at Oreton Common. Intriguingly, Jorden did not mention this in his own list for the area in 1856. In 1894 Richard Benson recorded it at Pulverbatch (SJ4202) and W.H. Painter found it at Kemberton (SJ7304). The only other record for the county was in 1961, when Edward Rutter saw it by the Cound Brook at Boreton (SJ5106).

It seems most likely that this plant would have been introduced into the county along roadsides, where it thrived in winter-wet, muddy conditions, but was never really suited to the climate. The improvement of road surfaces and the development of motor cars virtually eliminated this habitat a century ago. Significantly, perhaps, there has been an increase in its range northwards in recent years, according to the New Atlas, which could be a response to climate change. The native range of Chamomile is around the Mediterranean, although it is sometimes considered native in parts of the south and west of Britain and Ireland.

Chenopodium ficifolium Sm.
Fig-leaved Goosefoot
Archaeophyte. Scarce.

This is an arable weed that is reasonably common in the south-east of Britain and has been expanding its range in recent decades. In Shropshire it was recorded by Edward Williams as 'common on dunghills and among potatoes' in 1800. There are then no good records for it until 1995, when Julie Clarke and Audrey Franks found it on a roadside verge at Woore (SJ7342). It has since been recorded by Rob Stokes at Stockton (SJ7716, 1996), Albrighton (SJ8203, 1997), Shrewsbury (SJ4915, 2000) and Madeley (SJ7004, 2000). Geoffrey Kitchener found it at Eaton Manor Farm (SO4990) in 2003. It seems likely to be more widespread in the county now than these records show

Chenopodium urbicum L.
Upright Goosefoot
Archaeophyte. Extinct (1841).

Two hundred years ago this was a fairly common weed in Britain, but it has been recorded in Shropshire only twice: Williams considered it to be 'not uncommon' on dunghills in about 1800, and Edward Elsmere recorded it on his farm at Hadnall (SJ5220) in 1841 (conf. Leighton).

Cicuta virosa L.
Cowbane
Native. Scarce.

Cowbane is a real speciality of Shropshire, with its distribution in England almost confined to the Shropshire-Cheshire plain, and only the Norfolk Broads providing any other stronghold for it. It is rare in Scotland, virtually absent from Wales, but abundant in parts of Ireland.

The earliest record of it in the county was in 1632, when George Bowles saw it at The Mere, Ellesmere (SJ4034). William Withering found it at Hatton (SJ7604) in 1787, and Edward Williams recorded it eleven sites in about 1800: Betton Pool (SJ5107), Bomere Wood (SJ5007), Cole Mere (SJ4333), Cound Hall (SJ5605), Crose Mere (SJ4230), Hencott Pool (SJ4916), Sandford Pool (SJ3524), Top Pool (SJ5207), Uckington Heath (SJ5610), Upton Magna (SJ5511) and Wolf's Head (SJ3620). Turner & Dillwyn (1805) had a record for Buildwas (SJ6304).

Leighton (1841) gives records for Hencott Pool (Leighton), The Mere (Bloxam),

Lightmoor (SJ6705, Brookes), Oxon Pool (SJ4513, Bowman) and Snowdon Pool (SJ7801, Dickinson). Both Phillips (1878) and Beckwith (1880) saw it at Hencott Pool and Beckwith added Norton (SJ5609, 1880), White Mere (SJ4132, 1880), Haughmond Abbey (SJ5415, 1882), Upton Magna (SJ5512, 1882) and Fenemere (SJ4422, 1882).

After this there was a lull in recording, with only three records during the next seventy years. Thomas Diamond listed it at Pentre-pant (SJ2831) and Rednal (SJ3628) in 1891 and Gilbert Johnson saw it at Bicton (SJ4414) in 1909.

Francis Rose heralded the modern era of recording in 1959 with a rediscovery at Fenemere, and this was followed by refinds at Hencott Pool (1962) and The Mere (1965) by Sinker. New sites were found at Marton Pool, Baschurch (SJ4423) by Fuller & Richards in 1968, Shrawardine Pool (SJ3916) by Sarah Stafford, Woore (SJ7140) & Bearstone (SJ7239) by Bryan Fowler, and Oss Mere (SJ5643) by Martin Wigginton.

It seems that Cowbane is not uncommon in small pools in the North Shropshire plain. Many of these are on private land in places such as Shavington (SJ6338) and Adderley (SJ6539) Parks (A.P. Bell, 1980). Access to such sites is restricted, and it tends to be recorded only when the area is being visited for a different purpose. For instance, a population of about 50 plants at Aychley Farm (SJ6134) was reported by the farmer, Julie Edwards (conf. Whild), when she attended a botany course in Shrewsbury, and it was found at New Park Farm, Shifnal (SJ7506) by ecological consultant Tim Pankhurst in 1999.

Seedlings are often found on the bare, muddy margins of pools and meres, often under an open canopy of W5 *Alnus glutinosa* woodland, but the mature plants also compete well amongst tall reeds and sedges. What seems to favour this species is a long-term fluctuation in water levels, as at Shrawardine Pool in recent years: in the late 1990s it completely dried up and scrubbed over, but by 2004 it was flooded to the extent that many of the trees had died, and there were huge populations of Cowbane on floating rafts of Yellow Iris *Iris pseudacorus* and Bogbean *Menyanthes trifoliata*.

There is no real evidence of an overall decline of Cowbane, but it does appear to have been lost from certain sites such as the Mere at Ellesmere, where the water level has long been stabilised and the margins are now densely wooded.

Cicuta virosa

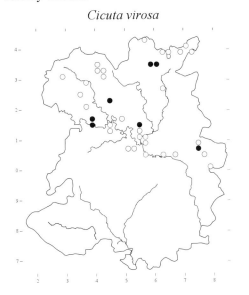

Circaea ×intermedia Ehrh.
(*C. alpina × lutetiana*)
Upland Enchanter's-nightshade
Native. Rare.

A hybrid between Enchanter's-nightshade *C. lutetiana* and Alpine Enchanter's-nightshade *C. alpina*, this species is often found growing in the absence of its parents, especially the latter, which is very rare in Britain. Upland Enchanter's-nightshade is found in wet woodlands, particularly in Wales, the north-west of England and Scotland.

It was first found in Shropshire by James Cosmo Melvill, when he found plants growing by the side of the Rea Brook at Meole Brace (SJ4810) in 1915. After puzzling over its identification for a couple of years, he sent specimens to the Botanical Exchange Club where it was misidentified as *C. alpina* by E.S. Marshall and W.H.

Pearsall. Melvill reluctantly agreed to this determination.

It was more than forty years later, in September 1960, that Charles Sinker & Francis Rose discovered the source of Melvill's plants beside the Habberley Brook, a tributary of the Rea, at Earl's Hill (SJ4104). Here *Circaea ×intermedia* grew in abundance in ancient W8 *Fraxinus excelsior* woodland. It has been recorded many times since then, most recently by Lockton *et al.* in June 2004, when it was still widespread but perhaps less abundant than formerly. In 1997 a third site was discovered near the source of the Habberley Brook at Upper Vessons, at SJ3802 (Whild & Lockton). This is possibly the original source of the downstream populations, and it is tempting to imagine *Circaea alpina* growing in this locality at the top of the Stiperstones range in the distant past.

Cirsium acaule (L.) Scop.
Dwarf Thistle
Native. Rare.

This is a small plant of short calcareous grassland, largely confined to the south-east of England. Although Sinker (1985) described it as occurring in 'long-established colonies' in Shropshire, there are no records of it prior to 1970 (except two highly dubious ones by G.H. Griffiths in 1870) and it appears to be spreading.

Doris Pugh first recorded it in a field on the edge of Llanymynech Hill (SJ2721) in 1970. Although it disappeared from that site, it has since been seen in several other locations on the hill, most recently by D. Guest & S. Smith in 1997.

In 1977 Cilla Raikes found it a field at Knowbury (SO5674), on the southern slopes of Titterstone Clee, and it was seen by Ellen Heywood-Waddington on a track side at Clee Hill (SO6075) the same year. Since then it has been recorded at Clee Hill by Trueman at SO5977 (1980) and by Bingham at SO6074 (1990 & 1997). In the latter site there were thousands of plants.

Audrey Ashwell found it in 1991 and 1992 at Cold Hatton Heath (SJ6320), where it grew on soil that had been dumped in a field.

Rob Stokes discovered it in a field adjacent to Stokes's Barn (SO6099) on Wenlock Edge in 1994, where it still was in 2003 (Whild, Lockton & Stokes). This brings the number of current sites in the county to four.

Cirsium dissectum (L.) Hill
Meadow Thistle
Native. Rare.

The characteristic habitat for this species in Shropshire seems to be on the edges of bogs and in wet meadows, often associated with the meres. The first records were by J.E. Bowman at the Mere, Ellesmere (SJ4034) and Blakemere (SJ4133) in about 1835. In 1841 Leighton recorded it 'sparingly' at Shawbury Heath (SJ5420).

Francis Rose & David Bellamy found it at Wem Moss (SJ4734) in 1959, where it was subsequently seen by Sinker in 1962, Ian Bonner & Colin Reynolds in 1968, and by Keith Bell in 1976. Bell described it as being in fen on the north-east side of the moss, but since the site became a nature reserve the marginal vegetation has been neglected, and it seems unlikely that the *Cirsium dissectum* could have survived.

Bryan Fowler recorded in a marshy pasture at Beamish (SJ8304) in 1976 and 1986. In 1993 Nigel Jones reported it from Cole Mere (SJ4333), where it has since been seen by Walker & Whild (1998) and Whild & Lockton (2000). A small patch occurs in a damp field to the north-east of the mere, and has flourished since the County Council introduced a regime of light grazing and hay meadow management.

Cirsium eriophorum (L.) Scop.
Woolly Thistle
Native. Scarce.

In Shropshire this species grows on the Silurian limestone, sometimes in areas where there has been some disturbance, such as in quarries and along tracks. It is also known to occur in woodland edges. It appears to have declined quite significantly in the last few decades, possibly due to the trend toward sharp boundaries between habitats, and the tidying up of roadside verges.

There are recent records of it at Pastycraft (SO5571, R. Mileto, 1994), where it was first recorded by Joyce Roper and Diana Kingham in 1978; at Marked Ash (SO5190, Whild & Lockton, 2003), where it has been known since Leighton's time; at Stokes's Barn (SO6099 & SJ6000, Whild, Lockton & Stokes, 2003), where it was first recorded by M.E. Chadd in 1977; and at Windmill Hill (SJ6200, Lockton, 2004), where it was recorded by William Penny Brookes in 1841.

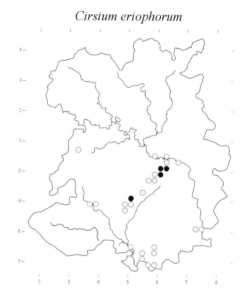

Cirsium eriophorum

Cladium mariscus (L.) Pohl
Great Fen-sedge
Native. Scarce.

The habitat for this species is peaty fenland with calcareous surface water. It has been recorded in nine sites in the county, but is probably now restricted to just four or five, and it is very rare except at Crose Mere.

Edward Williams recorded it in abundance at Cole Mere (SJ4333) in about 1800, where it was subsequently seen by Henry Bidwell (conf. Leighton) in 1841, but not since then. Williams also had it at Rednal Moss (SJ3427).

J.E. Bowman first recorded it at Crose Mere (SJ4230) in 1836, where it has subsequently been seen many times. It was still locally frequent around the western half of the lake in 2003 (Lockton & Whild). In Diamond's Flora of Oswestry (1891) there is a record for The Mere, Ellesmere (SJ4034), made by the Oswestry & Welshpool Naturalists, but it has never been recorded there since.

William Phillips first recorded it at Berth Pool (SJ4223) in 1892, and it was also recorded there by Pat Parker in 1988. William Beacall saw it in a 'pool near Marton' in 1902 – possibly also Berth Pool.

In Sinker's Flora there is a record for 'Lyneal' that was apparently in Hamilton's manuscript Flora of 1913. This could be a reference to Cole Mere or perhaps to Lyneal Moss (SJ4334). In 1970 Sinker found it at Birchgrove Pool (SJ4323), where it has since been recorded by Wigginton (1980) and Stokes (1994).

Will Prestwood and Chris Walker first recorded it at The Yesters (SJ4322) – a partially drained wetland in the Fenemere fens – where it was later seen by Pat Parker & Ruth Dawes in 1993. A tiny clump of plants was revealed at Fenemere recently when a new fishing platform was installed (SJ4423, Lockton, 2003).

Cladium mariscus

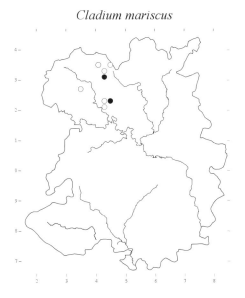

Clinopodium ascendens (Jord.) Samp.
Common Calamint
Native. Scarce.

This is a plant of dry, calcareous soils in the south of Britain. It is recorded on roadside verges, in quarries, and sometimes in grassland. It appears to be something of a casual in Shropshire, where it is on the edge of its range.

Edward Williams recorded it in six places in about 1800: in Sheinton Churchyard (SJ6103); on the sides of roads at Coalbrookdale (SJ6604), Harnage (SJ5604), Minsterley (SJ3705); between Uffington and Sundorne (SJ5214); and on Haughmond Hill (SJ5413). Leighton (1841) gives six more localities: Lincoln's Hill, Coalbrookdale (SJ6703, Dickinson), Redhill (SJ4609), West Felton (SJ3425), Fields near Bomere Pool (SJ4908), Sharpstones Hill (SJ4909), and Ludlow (SO5174). In 1842 Frederic Westcott also recorded it at Ludlow, 'on the banks of castle walk.' It was still there in 1905 (J.C. Melvill), in 1951 (R.C. Palmer) and in 2001 (A.K. Thorne).

There is a specimen at HLU, collected in 1862 (probably by John Fraser) at Bridgnorth (SO7192), where it has since been seen by Beckwith (1880), G.A. Audley (1902) and Joan Brown (SO7294, 1991 & 1992). In 1878 William Phillips revisited it at Bomere and Haughmond Hill. Beckwith added Uffington (SJ5213) to the list of sites in 1880; Audley saw it at Harnage again in 1902; W.B. Allen had it at Wyke (SJ6402) in 1903; George Potts found it at Haughton (SO6795) in 1904; and G.E. Johnson recorded it at Forton (SJ4316) in 1909. There were two other sites given in Hamilton's manuscript Flora of 1913, but we do not have the details.

The first record for the north-west of the county was in 1954, when Margaret Asterley found it at Pant (SJ2722). If this was on a roadside it soon spread to the quarries on Llanymynech Hill (SJ2621) on the Welsh side of the border, but has only been recorded in Shropshire by Helen Vickers in 1987, Kate Thorne in 1991 and Rob Stokes in 1994. It was still present in Pant in 1988 (Allan Dawes) and 1994 (Celia Chaffey).

J.B. Lawson found it at Bayston Hill (SJ4808) in 1956; Frank Perring & David Stones saw it at Netchwood (SO6292) in 1974; John Bingham recorded it at Highley-Alveley Country Park (SO7584) in 2001. It seems to be reasonable to consider it a wayside plant at most, if not all, of these sites, but if it is on the increase it may establish itself more firmly in the county.

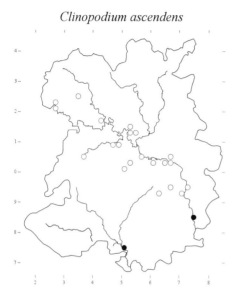

Clinopodium ascendens

Coeloglossum viride (L.) Hartm.
Frog Orchid
Native. Scarce.

This species has suffered one of the most dramatic declines of any in Shropshire. Leighton (1841) described it as not uncommon, and listed 15 sites from Oswestry to Ludlow. It is a plant of dry, calcareous grassland, and it was once quite frequent along Wenlock Edge, but it appears to have been lost from there entirely.

Edward Williams recorded it in meadows at Eaton Mascott (SJ5305) and Battlefield (SJ5116) in about 1800. Joseph Babington in 1803 considered it to be common in some meadows near Ludlow (SO5174), but rare elsewhere.

In Leighton's Flora of 1841 there are other records for Bomere Wood (SJ5007, Leighton), Buildwas (SJ6304, Harriet Moseley), Caynham Camp (SO5473, J. Walcot), Coalbrookdale (SJ6604, Francis

Dickinson), Hadnall (SJ5220, Edward Elsmere), Oreton (SO6580, Jorden), Oswestry (SJ2929, Salwey), Rowley (SO5999, Brookes), Shawbury Heath (SJ5420, T.W. Wilson), Wenlock Edge (SO5998, Leighton), Westhope (SO4786, Leighton) and Woodside (SJ7810, Henry Bidwell).

In the 1880s William Beckwith recorded it at Eaton Constantine (SJ5906), Longwood (SJ6007), Spout Lane (SJ6306), Harley (SJ6000) and on Wenlock Edge near Easthope (SO5998).

It is recorded in Diamond's Flora of 1891 at Crose Mere (SJ4330). Augustin Ley collected it at Bouldon (SO5485) in 1893 (BIRM). A certain Miss Attlee found it at Middleton Scriven (SO6887) in 1901. By this time it was noteworthy enough that all records were published. George Potts and W.B. Allen found it at Benthall (SJ6602) in 1902. 1904 seems to have been a good year for it: there are records for Underton Farm (SO6892, Potts), Eaton-under-Heywood (SO4989, W.E. Thompson), Lutwyche (SO5594, William Beacall) and Upper Millichope (SO5289, William Phillips).

Sinker (1985) reports that there were additional records in Hamilton's Flora of 1913 for the tetrads SJ43G, SJ50L & F, SJ80C, SO59A & L, but we do not know the details.

Apart from Salwey's vague record for the Oswestry district, it was not actually recorded in the north-west of the county until Ellen Lloyd found it at Craignant (SJ2535) and Llynclys & Llanymynech Hills (SJ2723 & SJ2622) in 1929. She also recorded it at Wern-ddu (SJ2326) in 1935.

It has never been abundant at Llynclys Hill. Doris Pugh reported in 1978 that there were just two or three flowering spikes most years, in short turf just below Jacob's Ladder. It crops up in various places around the hill, mostly in grazed fields outside the reserve. Allan Dawes reported finding two plants outside the boundary and just one inside in 2004.

It was first recorded at Craig Sychtyn (SJ2325) by Stan Turner in 1971, where it has since been recorded many times, including by Ned Wolfe in 1974, Doris Pugh in 1978, Pat Parker & Chris Walker in 1991, and by Ruth and Allan Dawes most years since then. The peak count was of 19 plants in 1998, but there were none at all in 2004 and there is concern that the site may be under-managed.

Coeloglossum viride

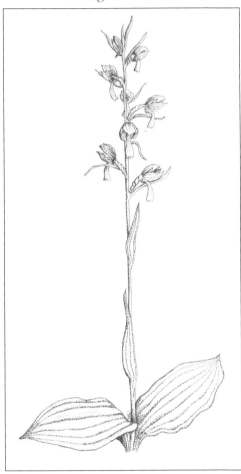

Another current site is Craig-llwyn Quarry (SJ2327), where it was first recorded in 1992 by Ros Gore. There were hundreds of plants, but by 2003 there was just one remaining (Tina Teearu & Ruth Dawes).

There are currently just six known sites for it in the county. The biggest population is in a meadow in Pant (SJ2723) where there were 171 plants (R.A. Dawes) in 2003. Another meadow, in Trefonen (SJ2526) was first

reported in 2004 (S. Swindells). It is an inconspicuous plant, and there may well be other undiscovered sites for it, but there is cause for concern, as it has declined so dramatically.

Coeloglossum viride

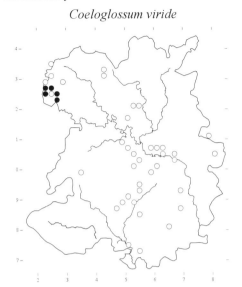

Cryptogramma crispa (L.) R.Br ex Hook.
Parsley Fern
Native. Rare.

This upland fern, which is fairly common in the mountains of northern England, Wales and Scotland, reaches its south-easterly limit on the hills of Shropshire. It was first recorded on Brown Clee (SO5986) by Joseph Babington in 1803, and was seen there again by the Reverend Prebendary W.G. Clark-Maxwell in 1926, who wrote 'in fair quantity, but in danger from the extension of the quarries.' It has not been seen there since.

The only other place where it has been recorded is at Titterstone Clee (SJ5978), where it was found by Edward Newman in 1854 'in four stations amongst the masses of basalt.' It has been recorded many times since, most recently by Clive Jermy in 2002.

Cuscuta epithymum (L.) L.
Dodder
Neophyte. Extinct (1984).

This is a parasitic plant with a wide range of hosts, often gorse or heather. Its range has contracted considerably in recent decades, and it is now restricted to the southern counties of England. In Shropshire it has been recorded as casual on crops and in gardens.

William Phillips first recorded it in a field at Burcotgate (SJ6110) in 1870. Beckwith & Serjeantson considered it to be naturalised on gorse at Charlton Hill (SJ5807) and Tentree Hill (SJ6604) in about 1880, and the latter collected a specimen at Kenley (SJ5600) in 1884. H.E. Forrest found it in a field of clover near Bomere Pool (SJ4908) in 1894 and John Ramsbottom also found it in a clover field at Prees Higher Heath (SJ5636) in 1907. There is apparently a record for Hencott Farm (SJ4815) in Hamilton's missing Flora of 1913, and a specimen from Wetmore (SO4477) was sent to Frances Pitt by a certain Miss Luce that same year. The only other record for the county dates from 1984, when Pat Parker recorded it as a pest in a garden at Westoncommon (SJ4226), after which it was eradicated by the owner.

[*Cynoglossum germanicum* Jacq.]
Green Hound's-tongue
Not in Shropshire.

In Leighton's Flora of 1841 there is a record of this species (as *C. sylvaticum*) by Mary McGhie, in the neighbourhood of Ludlow (SO5175). It is best regarded as an error. Charles Darwin's tentative record of the same species in Shrewsbury (SJ4711), in a letter to Leighton in 1841, includes a description that shows that this was also incorrect. There are therefore no confirmed records of this species in the county.

×Dactylodenia legrandiana (E.G. Camus) Peitz
Native. Extinct (1902).

The only record of this hybrid between *Dactylorhiza maculata* and *Gymnadenia conopsea* in Shropshire was by William Whitwell in 1902 (conf. E.F. Linton) at Oswestry (ca. SJ2929). Like other hybrids, it may be under-recorded.

Dactylorhiza *×halleri* (Druce) Soó
(*Dactylorhiza maculata × praetermissa*)
Native. Rare.

Dr H.V. Hughes noticed this unusual orchid growing with its parents in a field at Whiston Farm near Albrighton (SJ7802), and following a visit by the Botanical Society on June 9th 2004, specimens and photographs were sent to Richard Bateman at the Natural History Museum for confirmation. Orchid hybrids are apparently not uncommon, and can sometimes be recognised by their greater size, but due to introgression there can be a continuous range in markings and colour. At least half a dozen 'good' hybrids were present in a field with many hundreds of Early Marsh-orchids and a few Heath Spotted-orchids.

Dactylorhiza *×kernerorum* (Soó) Soó
(*Dactylorhiza fuchsii × incarnata*)
Native. Rare.

John Box collected a specimen of this hybrid orchid at Muxton Marsh (SJ7113) in 1986 and sent it to Peter Hunt at Kew for identification. The following year he found it at Donnington Hall (SJ7012). Similar plants were present in Waxhill Meadow at Granville Country Park (SJ7112) in 2000 & 2004 (Whild & Lockton, conf. R.M. Bateman). The spikes of this spectacular orchid are over 30cm high, and despite this being a well-used urban nature reserve, the majority of people seem to be careful not to pick or damage them. In 2004, however, Stephen Lewis, reported that the main population had been stolen, but a few remained in a corner of the field.

Dactylorhiza purpurella (T. & T.A. Stephenson) Soó
Northern Marsh-orchid
Native. Rare.

This is a common species of wet pastures in the north and west of Britain, but it is on the very edge of its range in Shropshire. The first record for the county was in 1937 when Maurice Gepp collected it in the Shelve area– probably at Black Marsh, near the headwaters of the West Onny at SO3299. Curiously, in 1953 Edward Rutter credited this discovery to H.H. Hughes and Sinker (1985) repeats that assertion; but we can find no trace of a record by Hughes. It was subsequently recorded at Black Marsh by Gepp again in 1940 and 1941, by Rutter in 1953, and by Sinker in 1970. Soon after that the site was destroyed by agricultural improvement.

The orchid, however, turned up again a couple of kilometres downstream at Brook House (SO3297) where it was discovered by Ned Wolfe in 1980 and subsequently seen by Chris Walker and Stan Turner in 1986.

Franklyn Perring recorded it at Attingham Park (SJ5409) in 1970, and Bryan Fowler found it at Sweeny Fen (SJ2725) in 1970 where it was also recorded by Packham & Trueman in 1979. A record for Caynton (SJ6920, R.B. Lees) in 1977 seems dubious.

The only currently known site for it in Shropshire is at the headwaters of the River Clun at The Riddings (SO1986), where 18 plants were found by Robin Smith in 2003.

Damasonium alisma Miller
Starfruit
Archaeophyte. Extinct (1842).

Starfruit is a fairly obvious archaeophyte in Britain, occurring in the past around village ponds in the south of England, to which it was presumably carried by horses and livestock coming over from the continent.

It was first recorded in Shropshire by Williams in about 1800 at The Mere, Ellesmere (SJ4034) and at Ebreywood (SJ5417). It has never been recorded anywhere else, although H.C. Watson in 1835 quoted J.E. Bowman stating that it was in most of the Shropshire meres. This was probably false, and Bowman never seems to have published such a statement himself. At The Mere it was recorded by John Evans (1805), Bowman (1835), Bloxam (1841) and finally by Henry Bidwell in 1842.

The site where it occurred was along the south shore of the mere, where there was an extensive common known as The Moors. The road there was used heavily in summer but became impassable in winter due to flooding.

After the canal was constructed in about 1800 this area was progressively drained, destroying the seasonally inundated habitat that Starfruit requires.

Deschampsia setacea (Huds.) Hack.
Bog Hair-grass
Native. Extinct (1894).

There is just one rather intriguing record of this very rare grass in Shropshire. It was found at Ellesmere (SJ4034) by F.A. Bellamy in 1894 and confirmed by Druce. If it was indeed this species it would most likely have been at The Moors, where there was once an extensive peat bog that used to become inundated in winter – precisely the sort of habitat that this species requires. Stabilisation of the level of the mere and drainage of The Moors has led to the almost complete destruction of this site, but many other rare glacial relics have been recorded there, and it is quite possible that Bog Hair-grass persisted until recent times. There is no suitable habitat remaining now, however.

Descurainia sophia (L.) Webb ex Prantl.
Flixweed
Archaeophyte. Rare.

This is a plant of disturbed ground such as arable fields and waste land. It occurs only sporadically in Shropshire, mostly along roadsides, and does not seem to persist.

Leighton had records for eight sites in 1841: Bayston Hill (SJ4808, Bodenham), Cressage (SJ5904, Brookes), Ness (SJ3919, Eyton), Ludlow (SO5175, McGhie), Pulley (SJ4709, Leighton), Shrewsbury (SJ4912, Leighton), Stanley (SO7195) and Wellington (SJ6511).

Phillips recorded it still at Bayston Hill and Pulley in 1878 and T.P. Blunt recorded it at Meole Brace (SJ4810) in 1900. George Potts found it in a chicken run at Benthall (SJ6602) in 1919. Beryl Davies found it on a roadside pavement in Oswestry (SJ2929) in 1984, and Will Prestwood saw several plants at the sugar beet factory at Allscott (SJ5912) in 1990.

Dianthus armeria L.

Deptford Pink

Archaeophyte. Extinct (1870).

This species, once common as a weed of agricultural and waste land, has only been recorded a few times in Shropshire as a casual. William Withering recorded it at Ketley (SJ6711) in 1787. Leighton (1841) has records for the canal bank at Burford (SO5968, W. Corbett); and for a roadside near Cleobury Mortimer (SO6775, M. McGhie). Alfred Marston recorded it at Greete (SO5770) and Ashford (SO5171) in 1870, and a Miss Blunt described it as 'almost wild' in a garden at Meole Brace (SJ4810) in 1923.

Dianthus deltoides L.

Maiden Pink

Native. Rare.

The native habitat of *Dianthus deltoides* is in the unimproved grassland of the NVC community U1 *Festuca ovina-Agrostis capillaris-Rumex acetosella* grassland, which is a significant element of the vegetation of Shropshire and the Welsh Marches. It is a short, open type of grassland, usually maintained by sheep grazing, and it is often restricted to south-facing slopes, where summer drought is the norm. Characteristic species of the community include *Moenchia erecta*, *Ornithopus perpusillus* and *Teesdalia nudicaulis*, which are still common on the unenclosed commons in the west.

The first record of *D. deltoides* in the county was by Littleton Brown in about 1725, along the road from Bishops Castle to Woodbatch (SO3188). Painter also saw it in this area in 1896. Aikin found it at Pulley Common (SJ4709) in 1796. At about the same time Williams recorded it at Davenport House near Bridgnorth (SO7595). Joseph Babington saw it near Church Stretton (SO4593) in about 1803. The Reverend J.M. Traherne recorded it at Quatford (SO7390) in 1809, where it was later seen by Thomas Purton in 1817, William Penny Brookes in about 1841, The Reverend G. Childe in 1843, Thomas Westcombe in 1845, and Frances Pitt in 1910. The only other record of it in this area

was by Henry Bidwell at The Walls, Chesterton (SO7896) in about 1841.

Williams also recorded it at Downton Quarry on Haughmond Hill (SJ5413), where it has subsequently been seen by Beckwith in 1882, J.E. Cooper in 1887, Stan Turner in 1986, Pat Parker in 1987 and finally by Ian Trueman in 1992; but it now seems to have gone from there.

The first record for the Long Mynd was also by Williams, who found it by the side of the road between Norbury and Linley (SO3592) in about 1800. Curiously, it turned up a couple of kilometres away at Wentnor (SO3892) in 1990, when Sylvia and Philip Kingsbury converted an old paddock into a garden. On the other side of the Long Mynd, at Church Stretton (SO4593), it was recorded by S.P. Mansel in 1841, by G.H. Griffiths in 1870, by Margaret Hall in 1924, by Helen Davidson in 1976 and by Joyce Warren in 1986. It has never been recorded on the common land of the Long Mynd, however, despite the abundance of apparently suitable grassland.

Babington found it at Bayston Hill (SJ4908) in 1832 and it was later seen there by Forrest in 1910, by W.G. Cross in 1944, and by Sinker in 1948. Leighton recorded it at Sharpstone Hill (SJ4909), where it was subsequently seen by Arthur and Miss K. White in 1923 and 1924.

Henry Spare recorded *D. deltoides* at Ludlow and Ludford in about 1841, but it has never been seen there since.

Beckwith found it at Dryton, east of Shrewsbury (SJ5806), in 1880, where there is still some promising habitat, especially by the old racecourse. O.M. Feilden made a record for the Ellesmere area (SJ3934) in 1920. Like Henry Spare's records for Ludlow, this gives rise to an isolated dot on the map, and it seems possible that it was another casual occurrence. James Cosmo Melvill's record for it 'spreading luxuriantly' in the grounds of Meole Brace Hall (SJ4810) in 1923 may have been of an introduced population. George Potts also recorded it as a casual on a roadside at Much Wenlock (SO6299) in 1902 and by Buildwas Bridge (SJ6404) in 1941.

In 1939 J.B. Johnson found a new site near Clun (SO3081). This could well have been the same roadside bank where it was recorded by K.M. Bird in 1957, by Joyce Warren in 1987 and by various recorders since then. It was still there in small quantities in 2003.

Sinker saw *D. deltoides* at Earl's Hill (SJ4104) in 1958, but it has not been seen there again. The soil seems highly suitable, but much of the best grassland has been lost to woodland since it became a nature reserve. At The Lump, Priestweston (SO2998), *D. deltoides* was apparently discovered as late as 1981, by Peter Benoit. It has been seen since then by Chris Walker (1983, 1984, 1990 & 1994), Sally Budd (1985), Andrew Gagg (1987), Gary Vergine (1993), and Kate Thorne (1990 & 2000).

In 2002 Tom Wall found it in a surprising place – on a dry stone wall at Pennerley, on the Stiperstones (SO3598). This is probably a casual occurrence, and it is unlikely to persist.

Dianthus deltoides now persists at just two 'native' sites (near Clun and The Lump, Priestweston) , where the total population may be no more than a few dozen plants.

Dianthus deltoides

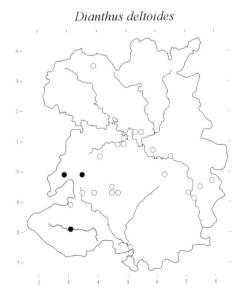

Diphasiastrum alpinum (L.) Holub

Diphasiastrum alpinum (L.) Holub
Alpine Clubmoss
Native. Extinct (1991).

The first record of this species in Shropshire was by Littleton Brown in June 1726, in a letter to Prof. Dillenius at Oxford. On 26th July that year Dillenius, Brewer and Brown visited the Stiperstones and saw it again, but it has never been seen there since.

Shropshire is on the extreme edge of the natural range of this upland species, which is fairly common in Scotland, northern England and Wales. It seems likely that its light, wind-blown spores must occasionally be deposited in the county, and this is probably how it arrived at an opencast coal mine at Stoneyhill in Telford (SJ6606), where it was discovered in 1984 by Richard Lamb. There it occurred on thinly-vegetated acidic mine waste with two other species of clubmoss, in some abundance. It only persisted for a short while, however, and was last seen in 1991 by John Box.

Diplotaxis tenuifolia (L.) DC.

Diplotaxis tenuifolia (L.) DC.
Perennial Wall-rocket
Archaeophyte. Extinct (1982).

The consensus is now that this species is an archaeophyte, introduced from temperate parts of Europe and widely established on waste ground and walls in Britain.

In Shropshire it was first recorded by Littleton Brown on the walls of Ludlow (SO5074) in about 1725, and it has been seen there many times since, notably by Babington (1803), Leighton (1841), Fraser (1874), Weyman (1893), Forrest (1919), Turner (1967), and Mrs J. Greenhalgh (1978). Leighton also had it at Shrewsbury Abbey (SJ4912) in 1841 and Beckwith reported it still there in 1882. Ian Bonner recorded it at Craven Arms (SO4382) in the 1970s, and Bill Thompson found a single plant on a disused railway at Ketley (SJ6710) in 1982, but it has not been recorded in the county since then.

Drosera anglica L.

Great Sundew

Native. Extinct (1998).

George Bowles & William Coote are sometimes credited with the first British record of this species, which they found by The Mere, Ellesmere (SJ4034) in 1632. It is not an uncommon species in the west of Scotland and Ireland, and it was once quite widespread in lowland England, but it has now declined almost to extinction, being very vulnerable to drainage and eutrophication.

In 1797 Edward Williams found it in the Rednal Moss complex near Queen's Head (SJ3426), where Leighton also saw it in about 1841. J.E. Bowman was the first to record it at Whixall Moss (SJ4936, 1841), where it has subsequently been seen by Beckwith (1889), Johnson & Feilden (1910), Jebb (1918), Forrest (1930) and Sinker (1970).

In 1844 Robert Garner recorded it at Gravenhunger Moss (SJ7342). In 1889 Beckwith found it in boggy ground near Hampton Bank – presumably Lyneal Moss (SJ4434), where it was also recorded by members of the 'Midland Union' in 1894. John Ramsbottom found it on Prees Heath in 1907.

Drosera anglica

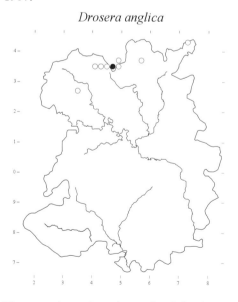

The two sites where it persisted for longest are Clarepool Moss (SJ4334) and Wem Moss (SJ4734). At Clarepool it was first recorded by Beckwith in 1880, and was subsequently

seen by Diamond *et al.* (1891), H. Stokes (1893), J.W. Heath (1894), Ellen Lloyd (1930), and by Francis Rose and David Bellamy in 1959, by which time there were only twelve plants remaining. Sinker saw it there in 1961, and in 1976 Keith Bell made the last definite record of it, in some peat cuttings on the north-west side.

The first record we have of it on Wem Moss (SJ4734) dates from 1950, when Edward Wilson recorded it there. It has also been recorded by Francis Rose & David Bellamy (1959), Charles Sinker (1962), Keith Bell (1976), Ian Trueman (1984), Jonathan Cox (1991), and Sarah Whild (1994, '95, '97 & '98), but it has not been seen there since.

Drosera intermedia Hayne

Oblong-leaved Sundew

Native. Extinct (1999).

The ecology of this species is similar to that of *D. anglica*, but its distribution is more southerly and it is generally found near the coast. It is also less likely to be found in upland areas.

In Shropshire it was first recorded by Edward Williams in 1798 at Shomere Pool (SJ5007), which at that time was surrounded by an extensive peat bog. There was another bog at Bomere Pool (SJ4908), where Williams also saw it at about the same time. It was subsequently seen at Shomere by Leighton in 1835, and at Bomere by John Evans (1805), Phillips (1878), and Beckwith (1880). Neither site has any suitable habitat today.

In 1805 Evans recorded it at Hatton on Hine Heath (SJ6024), and in 1841 Eyton recorded it on a moss near Cold Hatton (SJ6321). These could be references to the same place, but there could also have been several suitable bogs in the extensive heathlands between the Tern and the Roden in this part of the county.

Bowman was the first to record it on Whixall Moss (SJ4936), where it was subsequently seen by Beckwith (1880) and Jebb (1918). Leighton (1841) found it at Twyford Vownog (SJ3426) – part of the Rednall Moss complex; and Robert Garner recorded it at Gravenhunger Moss (SJ7342) in 1844. In

1880 Beckwith recorded it on Clarepool Moss, and in 1891 Diamond listed it for there.

The only recent site for it is Wem Moss (SJ4734), where it was discovered by Edward Rutter and James Lawson in 1957, and has since been seen by Rose & Bellamy (1959), Sinker (1962), K.K. Bell (1976), J.H.S. Cox (1991), and Whild (1994, '95 & '98). In 1999 Anne Bodley & Anne Cole counted 30 plants there, but it seems likely that it has now gone from there, as the moss has dried out considerably in recent years.

Drosera intermedia

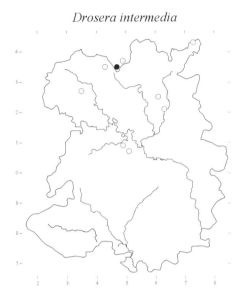

Drosera ^x*obovata* Mert. & Koch
(*D. anglica* × *rotundifolia*)
Hybrid Sundew
Native. Extinct (1965).

This was recorded by Sinker at Clarepool Moss (SJ3443) in 1965 and Wem Moss (SJ4734) in 1962.

Dryopteris aemula (Aiton) Kunze
Hay-scented Buckler-fern
Native. Extinct (1858).

In 1858 J. Hayes and R. Anslow apparently recorded this species at La Mole (Loamhole) Pool (SJ6604), but it has not been seen in the county again.

Dryopteris oreades Fomin
Mountain Male-fern
Native. Rare.

This upland fern occurs in northern England, Wales and Scotland, but is entirely absent from England south of Lancashire except for two sites in Shropshire. It was recorded at Titterstone Clee (SO5978) by Sinker in 1962, and his specimen in Shrewsbury Museum was confirmed by A.C. Jermy in 1962 and again in 2000, but it was not reliably recorded there again until John Bingham found it in 2002 (conf. Jermy). The second site was discovered by Sarah Whild in 2002 on Earl's Hill (SJ4104, conf. F.J. Rumsey). There is just one plant at each location, making this possibly the rarest species in the county.

Elatine hexandra (Lapierre) DC.
Six-stamened Waterwort
Native. Rare.

Edward Williams is credited with the first British record of this species at Bomere Pool (SJ4908) in 1798. It grows in the margins of lakes and pools with a fluctuating water level that leaves it exposed on bare mud during the summer. It appears to be a good indicator of clear, unpolluted water.

It has been recorded at Bomere Pool many times since Williams found it, notably by Bowman (1832), Phillips (1874), Serjeantson (1880), Melvill (1918), Rutter (1955), Wigginton (1979), Walker (1985 & 1994) and Whild (2003). It is still frequent around the north and east margins, although the water level has been stabilised and the edge of the water is now increasingly shaded by trees, giving cause for concern for its conservation there.

The only other site in the county where it now occurs is Newton Mere (SJ4234), where it was first recorded by Beckwith in 1889, and has since been seen by Wigginton (1979) and Stokes (1994). In the past it was known at The Mere, Ellesmere (SJ4034, Bowman, 1841) and White Mere (SJ4132, Serjeantson & Beckwith, 1880).

Eleocharis acicularis (L.) Römer
  & Schultes
Needle Spike-rush
Native. Rare.

A lowland plant that occurs on the margins of lakes, rivers and canals, often exposed on bare mud in the summer. Edward Williams recorded it in five meres and pools in about 1800: Sundorne Pool (SJ5215), by the Roden at Rodington (SJ5914), at Betton Abbots Pool (SJ5108), Cole Mere (SJ4333) and White Mere (SJ4132). The only one of these where it has been recorded again is White Mere, where it has been seen by Dickinson (1841), Wigginton (1979), and Walker (1985-1992).

Bowman and Bloxam both recorded it at The Mere, Ellesmere (SJ4034) in Leighton's Flora of 1841, and it has since been seen there by Beckwith (1880), Sinker (1965) Wigginton (1979) and Whild *et al.* (1997).

Beckwith found it on the muddy margins of the Severn at Leighton (SJ6004) in 1882. This was only the second record of it in a river in the county. In 1963 Sinker found it for the first time in a canal, the Prees Branch of the Llangollen Canal (SJ4924), where J.M. Way also collected it that year. It has not been seen there again. The only other recent record of it in the county was along a newly-restored section of the Montgomery Canal at Keeper's Bridge (SJ3528) where Richard Lansdown found it in 1998. It has probably gone from there following the re-opening of the canal to navigation, leaving just two current sites for it in the county: White Mere and Ellesmere. A record for Ratlinghope Hill (SO4097, J.A. Warren & H.M. Davidson, 1991) is surely an error.

Eleocharis multicaulis (Sm.) Desv.
Many-stalked Spike-rush
Native. Scarce.

There is only one record of this westerly, oceanic species in Leighton's Flora of 1841: Edward Elsmere had found it at Shawbury Heath (SJ5420, det. Leighton); but it has never been seen at that site again. There are no more records until 1904, when W.E. Thompson apparently recorded it in a bog above Light Spout Hollow on the Long

Mynd – presumably Boiling Well (SO4294). There has to be some suspicion that Thompson confused it with *Eleocharis quinqueflora*, as the latter is well-known on the Long Mynd, while *E. multicaulis* has not been seen there before or since.

In 1959 Francis Rose and David Bellamy discovered it at Wem Moss (SJ4734), where it was later seen by Sinker in 1962 & 1970, but not since then. The only other site for it in the north of the county was Brown Moss (SJ5639), where it was found by Sinker in 1965 but has not been seen since.

The only current sites for it are around Titterstone Clee, where it is recorded in 7 1km squares. Edward Rutter was the first to record it there, at Catherton Common (SO6378) in 1962, where it has since been recorded by Sinker (1965, 1983 and Bingham, 1991). Elsewhere, it has been seen at Gorstley (SO5874, Bingham, 1990), Clee Hill (SO5975, Bingham, 1991 & 1997), Cornbrook (SO6075, Bingham, 1997), Silvington Common (SO6278, Trueman, 1998) and Cramer Gutter, both inside the reserve (SO6479, Prestwood & Trueman, 1989; Perring, 1989; Bingham, 1995; and Whild, 1998 & 2004) and outside (SO6579, Bingham, 1995).

Eleocharis multicaulis

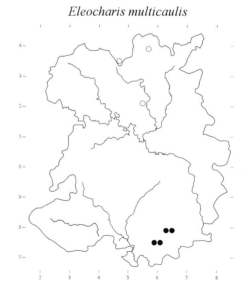

Eleogiton fluitans (L.) Link
Floating Club-rush
Native. Scarce.

Although this is not a rare species in Britain, it has declined significantly in agricultural lowlands and it is now very rare in the Midlands. It occurs in acid, peaty ditches and streams.

Edward Williams found it in ditches associated with mires in the north of the county, in about 1800: Berrington Pool (SJ5207), Betton Pool (SJ5107), Birch (SJ4033), Bomere Pool (SJ4908), Hencott Pool (SJ4916), Rednal Moss (SJ3427), Shomere Pool (SJ5007), and The Mere, Ellesmere (SJ4034). All of those meres had raised mires along their margins in Williams's day, but only Shomere still has any trace remaining today. In Leighton's Flora of 1841 there are also records for a pit at Astley (SJ5218, T.W. Wilson & E. Elsmere, conf. Leighton), and Hencott Pool (Leighton).

Griffith Griffiths re-recorded it at Bomere Pool in about 1870, while Phillips saw it still there and at Hencott Pool and Astley in 1878. Robert Serjeantson found a new site at Shawbury Heath (SJ5420) in 1882, and William Allen found it in a bog near Ashfield (SO5889) in 1904. Philip Nethercott recorded it on Stapeley Hill (SO3199) in 1958.

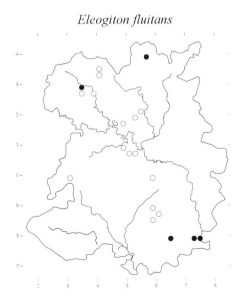

Eleogiton fluitans

It was first found at Brown Moss by Charles Sinker in 1961, and has since been recorded there by Keith Bell (1975), Will Prestwood (1977), Chris Walker (1981-1985), Ian Trueman (1983-1996), Frank Perring (1993) and Sarah Whild (1999). The habitat has deteriorated so much that it seems certain to have gone from there now.

Perring first recorded it at Boyne Water (SO5884) in 1976, where it was later seen by Mary Fuller in 1986. Trueman discovered it in the stream at Cramer Gutter (SO6479) in 1980, where it has since been recorded by Walker (1985) and Bingham (1988-1995).

In 1979 John Bingham found it in a stream at Lawley's Coppice in the Wyre Forest (SO7378), but the record was omitted from Sinker's Flora, presumably because the coordinator of that square did not believe it. However, it was still there in 1995, and further along the stream at Birchen Vallets (SO7479).

Kate Thorne found an interesting new site for it in 2003, at Wootton (SJ3428). This is an agricultural ditch in lowland farmland. Sinker (1985) gives two other dots on his distribution map, for SJ32Y and SO59Z, which are derived from records in Hamilton's lost Flora of 1913.

This species is therefore known in just six sites in the county at present. It has suffered a serious decline, and it is indicative of clean, acidic flowing waters – one of the most threatened habitats in the county.

Epipactis leptochila (Godfrey) Godfery
Narrow-lipped Helleborine
Native. Extinct (1993).

An uncommon species of open limestone woodland and a variety of other specialised habitats. It has a very limited distribution, scattered in England & Wales. It is difficult to give a definitive account of this species because the taxonomy has changed over the years and identification is not always straightforward. It is probably this species (as *E. viridiflora*) that Babington and Leighton found in the woods west of Bomere Pool (SJ4908) in 1832 and 1835. Babington's 1841 record for Oswestry (ca. SJ22) may have been for the same species. In a paper in The North Western Naturalist in December 1940, L.C. Lloyd cites records from 'one or two stations in the county' (attributed to Godfrey 1933) but these stations remain unknown.

In 1972 David Stoves recorded it in Lower Netchwood (SO6291). In 1978 Audrey Ashwell collected it in Blakeway Coppice on Wenlock Edge (SO5897); it was still there in 1993 but has not been seen since, despite several searches.

Epipactis palustris (L.) Crantz
Marsh Helleborine
Native. Rare.

The first record of this species in Shropshire was by 'a student of Physick' (probably Littleton Brown) in the 1720s, at Oakeley Wood (SO3488). Edward Williams found it in a boggy field near Cound Moor (SJ5502) in about 1800, and John Evans recorded it in a wood on his estate at Llwyn-y-groes (SJ2820) at the same time.

In Leighton's Flora of 1841 it is listed for Rowley (SO5999, William Brookes, conf. Leighton), Cantern Rough (SO7094, George Lloyd) and Felton Farm (SO5076, Mary McGhie). In 1856 George Jorden recorded it in the Wyre Forest (ca. SO7576), but possibly not on the Shropshire side.

In 1880 Robert Serjeantson found it at Church Preen (SO5498), and in 1882 Beckwith recorded it in a field under Wenlock Edge near Harley (SJ5901) – possibly the same site as W.P. Brookes's. It was later recorded at nearby Homer (SJ6101) by George Potts in 1912 and 1929, suggesting a cluster of calcareous fens in this area. Beckwith also found it at Crose Mere (SJ4230), where it was later recorded by Diamond (1891), E.A. Wilson (1950), Rutter (1953), Sinker (1960), Keith Bell (1976) and Chris Walker (1980).

In 1901 W.B. Allen recorded it at Thonglands (SO5589). In 1903 George Potts found it near Byelet Coppice (SO6596), where it has since been recorded by Potts again in 1921 and 1936; by Chris Walker & Ian Bolt in 1977; and by Rob Mileto in 1994. In 1904 William

Beacall found it near Wentnor (SO3892); and in 1920 and 1921 Oswald Feilden recorded it near Ellesmere (ca. SJ3934) and at Welsh Frankton (SJ3633).

It was Ian Bonner who first recorded it at Sweeny Fen (SJ2725) in 1966, and it has subsequently been recorded there by Bryan Fowler (1970), Chris Walker (1977-1986), Doris Pugh (1978), John Packham (1979), Frank Perring (1989) and Marjorie Wainwright (1991-1999). The site is a Wildlife Trust reserve, and although it is fenced off and tending towards scrub, the paths trampled by numerous visitors seem to create enough open habitat for it, and it was still abundant there in 2004 (Whild & Lockton). The vegetation seems to be predominantly M27 *Filipendula ulmaria-Angelica sylvestris* mire.

Apart from Byelet Coppice and Sweeny Fen, the only other current site for it is at Trefonen Marshes (SJ2426), where it was first recorded by Doris Pugh in 1979, and was still there in 2003 (Ruth Dawes).

Epipactis palustris

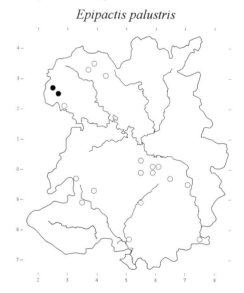

Epipactis phyllanthes G.E. Sm.
Green-flowered Helleborine
Native. Rare.

The only site for this species in Shropshire is Benthall Edge Wood (SJ6503 & SJ6603), where it used to occur in small numbers along the edges of tracks in a couple of places. It was first recorded by Sir Paul

Benthall in 1963 (conf. D.P. Young), and has since been recorded many times, but the last record we have dates from 1998 (Rob Stokes) and that plant is known to have gone, leaving this species possibly extinct in the county. A dot in SJ30 in *Scarce Plants* was probably an error and does not appear in the New Atlas.

Epipogium aphyllum Sw.
Ghost Orchid
Native. Extinct (1892).

There are persistent rumours of this species still occurring in one or two places in England, but no confirmed records since 1986. It grows in beech and oak woods, and its inconspicuous flowering stems would be very easily overlooked, so there is every chance that it is still present. In most of its known sites it was discovered by children playing in the woods. The Shropshire site was found by a Miss Lloyd in 1876 and a Miss Peele also collected it there two years later. Babington saw it there in 1881, and Druce was the last to see it in 1892. The precise locality was a wood called Upper Evens (SO4973) in Mortimer Forest, which is mostly in the modern county of Herefordshire but is in vice county 40.

[*Equisetum* ×*font-queri* Rothm.]
(*E. palustre* × *telmateia*)
Skye Horsetail
Not in Shropshire.

This hybrid has only been recorded in a few places in Britain, most notably on Skye, where it forms large and vigorous stands. The only record for Shropshire was by A.R. Busby in 1983 by the Montgomery Canal at Queen's Head (SJ338266), but it has never been seen there again, despite many searches, and no voucher specimen is known. It seems possible that this record might have been an error.

Equisetum hyemale L.
Rough Horsetail
Native. Extinct (1877).

There are records of Rough Horsetail by a stream at Cantlop Wood (SJ5104) by Edward

Williams in about 1800; in a dell at Bitterley (SO5677) by Thomas Moore in 1862; and at Town Mills in Bridgnorth (SO7294) by a Miss Brown in 1877. All of these are seemingly by streams, which is the natural habitat of this species, so it must be assumed that it was native, although it was apparently also cultivated at one time.

Eriophorum latifolium Hoppe
Broad-leaved Cottongrass
Native. Rare.

This is a plant of calcareous fens that has declined markedly in lowland England, although it is still common in Britain in upland areas. In Shropshire it was first recorded by Edward Williams at Mosterley (SJ5502) and Vessons Wood (SJ3801) in about 1800. Francis Dickinson found it in one of the bogs at the base of the Wrekin in 1841 and Waties Corbett saw it at Coreley (SO6173) at about the same time. Edward Elsmere recorded it at Astley (SJ5218) in 1841, where William Phillips saw it again in 1878. William Beacall found it at Easthope Wood (SO5695) in 1886.

Eriophorum latifolium

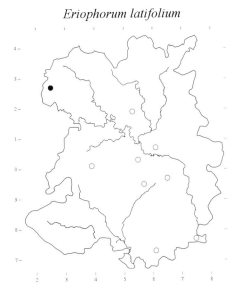

A specimen collected by J.H. Thompson in the Wyre Forest (ca. SO7577) some time before 1889 was determined by William Hunt Painter in 1905. In the same year George

Potts and W.B. Allen found it at Shirlett (SO6597).

In 1980 Chris Walker discovered it at Trefonen Marshes (SJ2426), where it still was in 2000 (R.M. Stokes) and Ian Trueman refound it at Shirlett. In 1986 John Bingham also rediscovered it in the Wyre Forest. It might still be present in all three of these sites.

Erodium maritimum (L.) L'Hér.
Sea Stork's-bill
Native. Extinct (1916).

Although this is mainly a coastal plant, it also occurs inland, usually in disturbed sandy areas. In Shropshire it was recorded by Williams in about 1800 near the Hermitage, Bridgnorth (SO7293) and at the south end of the Wrekin (SJ6307). Mary McGhie collected it at the foot of the Long Mynd (SO49) in about 1841 (conf. Leighton). In 1916 J.B. Duncan also saw it at Bridgnorth, but that is the last record for the county.

Erodium moschatum (L.) L'Hér.
Musk Stork's-bill
Archaeophyte. Rare.

In 1796 Arthur Aikin 'met with' this species near Montford Bridge (SJ4414) on the start of his tour of North Wales. At about the same time Edward Williams recorded it more precisely: 'on the right hand side of the road as you ascend the bank from Bicton towards Montford Bridge.' In 1840 Thomas Du Gard found it at Lilleshall (SJ7315); and in 1841 Dovaston recorded it on Ellesmere Bowling Green (SJ4034) and Edwin Lees saw it in the lane leading from Wellington to the Wrekin (SJ6511). Holland Sandford collected a specimen at Whitchurch (SJ5441) in about 1849.

In 1980 Bryan Fowler found it in a sand quarry near Condover (SJ4804), and in 1998 we (Whild & Lockton) found it on the banks of the Severn near Montford (SJ4214), not far from the original site recorded by Aikin and Williams. All the places it has been found in are probably sandy, but whether it is strictly a casual in the county, or rare and persistent, is not known.

Euphrasia anglica Pugsley
Eyebright
Native. Extinct (1955).

This species occurs in short grassland in lowland areas in southern England, South Wales and western Ireland. It has been collected twice in Shropshire and, curiously, both of these records date from 1955. Apparently a certain A. Martin found it in a field near Betchcott (SO4498) and Edward Rutter collected it in a marshy meadow near Harton (SO4888). Both specimens (GGE & SHY respectively) have been determined by P.F. Yeo. The field near Betchcott was reported by Joyce Warren to have been ploughed by 1986, but we have no information on the fate of the second site.

Euphrasia arctica Lange ex Rostrup
Eyebright
Native. Rare.

In the New Atlas this plant is recorded under two taxa – ssp. *arctica* is treated as very rare and mapped only in Orkney and Shetland, while all other records are mapped as ssp. *borealis*, which turns out to be rather common, in Scotland, northern England and Wales. There is, however, an admission that this simple division is probably not correct.

The first record for Shropshire was by Vera Gordon in 1956. She collected it on a lane side near Oswestry (ca. SJ2929), and the specimen was determined by E.F. Warburg as *E. arctica* ssp. *borealis*. In 1984 Sinker collected it at Pennerley Meadows (SO3599) and on the spoil heaps of an old lead mine nearby (SO3598). He considered this also to be ssp. *borealis* and it is listed as such in his Flora. However, plants collected at Pennerley Meadows in 1997 by Sarah Whild were identified by A.J. Silverside as ssp. *arctica*, which would represent a considerable increase on its known range in Britain.

In 1986 John Bingham recorded what he considered to be ssp. *borealis* in two species-rich grasslands in the Wyre Forest (SO7077 & SO7577), but these have not been independently confirmed.

Euphrasia micrantha Rchb.
Eyebright
Native. Extinct (1936).

This is one of the more common species of eyebright in Britain, occurring on acid heaths and moorland in the west. There is a specimen at Cambridge (det. P.F. Yeo) from Dovaston Heath (SJ3421) in 1839 – which we presume was collected by Leighton, as he is the only botanist known to have recorded at that site.

In 1936 R.C.L. Burges collected a specimen on a canal bank at Whixall – either the Prees Branch Canal or the Llangollen, so a grid reference of about SJ4835 seems reasonable. This record was confirmed by H.W. Pugsley.

In 1975 Franklyn Perring recorded it on a spoil heap at White Grit (SO3198) and in 1991 Bert Webster recorded it at Llanymynech Hill (SJ2621), but neither of these has been confirmed.

Euphrasia rostkoviana Hayne
Eyebright
Native. Rare.

There is only one recent record of this species in Shropshire. It was collected in the species-rich grassland along the path of the Wye Elan pipeline through the Wyre Forest (SO7077) by Sarah Whild & John Bingham in 1998 (conf. A.J. Silverside). Sinker (1985) reports that there are older records for the Wyre Forest, but no details are known.

Other records for Shropshire are by Painter (Church Stretton, SO4593, 1897), Melvill (Stokesay, SO4381, 1904), and Sinker & Perring (Batholes Meadow, SJ3300, 1962).

Euphrasia scottica Wettst.
Eyebright
Native. Extinct (1911).

J.C. Melvill recorded this species in Carding Mill Valley (SO4494) in 1907, 1909 and 1911. In the last year he saw it the bog had dried out and the plants were very small. It is not known whether any specimens still exist. Although Melvill seemed very positive about the identification, Lloyd & Rutter (1957) considered it doubtful and Sinker (1985)

ignored it completely. It is, however, mapped in the New Atlas.

[Euphrasia stricta D. Wolff ex J.F. Lehm.]
Eyebright
Not in Shropshire.

In 1907 William Hunt Painter collected a specimen at Buildwas (SJ6304) that was determined by J.W. White as Euphrasia officinalis var. stricta, which is presumably E. stricta, but the location of the specimen is unknown and that species has never been properly recorded in Britain.

Festuca altissima All.
Wood Fescue
Native. Scarce.

The habitat of this plant is in humid, wet woodland in deep valleys, on neutral or slightly calcareous soils, usually within the splash zone of a stream or waterfall. Although Sinker (1985) mentions earlier rumours of its occurrence in south Shropshire, Bill Thompson was the first to formally record it in 1981 - a small patch in a steep wooded gully at Ray's Bridge (SO7183) in 1981, where it still was in 2004 (Lockton).

A couple of weeks later he found a rather larger population in similar woodland alongside the Borle Brook near Highley (SO7383), and that was also still extant in 2004 (Lockton). In 1987 Chris Walker found it in Lydebrook Dingle (SJ6606), where it has since been recorded by Kate Thorne (2004).

A fourth site was found in 2004 when Wendy Compson & Alex Lockton collected it in Oaks Wood (SJ4104, det. S.J. Whild), by a tributary of the Habberley Brook. All the known sites are in ancient W8 Fraxinus excelsior woodland.

One other record for the county seems rather dubious. In 1977 J.L. Bostock and J.D. Box apparently recorded it 'in a flooded area in Donnington by a colliery tip.' The grid reference seems to relate to Muxton Marsh, where there is a large population of Festuca *arundinacea*, and it seems possible that this might have been a typographical error.

Festuca altissima

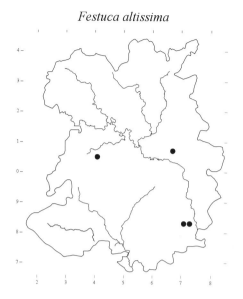

Filipendula vulgaris Moench
Dropwort
Native. Rare.

Edward Williams first recorded this species 'round the limestone quarries at Farley' in about 1800. This is typical habitat for it: dry, calcareous soils and closely-grazed chalk or limestone grassland. Williams's site was possibly Gleedon Hill (SJ6201), which is part of the same Silurian limestone formation as Wenlock Edge. It was subsequently seen there by W.P. Brookes in about 1841, by Beacall in 1891, by Rutter in 1954, and finally by B.W. Wood in 1976, in an old quarry that was in the process of being re-opened. Gleedon Quarry has since been closed, but there is no trace of *F. vulgaris* there.

A second site occurs about 1km to the south, at Windmill Hill (SJ6200). This could be the locality mentioned by Beckwith in 1880 and 1889 – 'rough ground by Olympian field, Much Wenlock.' If so, it was refound by D. Wood and J. Sankey in 1988, and has subsequently been seen again by Wood in 1992, by Rob Stokes in 1993 & 1995 and by Sarah Whild in 2004.

Bob Kemp found it in an unimproved meadow by the Borle Brook (SO7481) in 1982 (where *Cirsium eriophorum* has also been recorded) but it has not been seen there since, despite several searches. More recently, Rob Stokes found it growing as a casual among garden waste at Hadley (SJ6811) in 1997.

[*Fumaria bastardii* Boreau]
Tall Ramping-fumitory
Not in Shropshire.

There has never been a confirmed record of this species in Shropshire. In their Handlist of 1957, Lloyd & Rutter reported that 'Mr Pugsley thought it should not be accepted for the county without fresh evidence.'

The earliest record was by Augustin Ley in 1881 at Ludford (SO5173), but Charles Babington considered his specimen to be *F. muralis*. In 1901 W.B. Allen recorded it at Lodge Farm, on the Willey Estate (SJ6600); Doris Pugh recorded it at Ty Stanley (SJ2826) in 1978 and at Ty-isa (SJ2426) in 1979; and in 1994 Pat Parker recorded it in Baschurch churchyard (SJ4221). None of these should stand as a first county record without a voucher specimen for confirmation.

Fumaria densiflora DC.
Dense-flowered Fumitory
Archaeophyte. Extinct (1912).

Druce was the first to record this species in the county, in a field near Shrewsbury Cemetery (SJ4811) in 1892. In 1902 Richard Benson found it in hedges near Stapleton (SJ4605, det. T.C.G. Rich, SHYB). In 1912 and 1913 Melvill collected it in shrubberies at Meole Brace Hall (SJ4810, conf. Pugsley). This is the last confirmed record.

In 1962 Perring apparently found it in arable land near Preston Montford (SJ4314), but for some reason this record did not make it into Sinker's Flora of 1985 – possibly because it was not properly confirmed? Two recent records by Dave Buckingham, at Yeaton Peverey (SJ4419, 1999) and Grafton (SJ4318) should also be considered possible, but unconfirmed. Sinker (1985) also lists an old record for Steventon near Ludlow, which may have come from Hamilton's Flora of 1913.

Fumaria officinalis ssp. *wirtgenii*
 (W.D.J. Koch) Arcang.
Common Fumitory
Native. Scarce.

This is the rarer subspecies of common fumitory that is apparently restricted to the east of England. It was recorded in Shropshire by J.C. Melvill in 1912 at Meole Brace (SJ4810, conf. H.W. Pugsley, CGE) and then by Melvill again in the Roman excavations at Wroxeter (SJ5608) between 1913 and 1924 (conf. Pugsley). Melvill was clearly of the opinion that it came up from long-buried seed, perhaps from a time when the climate was warmer.

In recent years it has reappeared in the county. There are confirmed records from Uffington (SJ5312, S.J. Whild, 2001, conf. T.C.G. Rich) and Berrington (SJ5207, Whild, 2003, conf. Rich), Much Wenlock (SJ6200, Lockton, 2004, conf. Whild) and Whiston Hall (SJ7802, Lockton & Whild, 2004). It is interesting to speculate that it might be spreading in the recent warm climate, but it could easily have been overlooked in the intervening years.

Fumaria painteri Pugsley
Painter's Fumitory
Native. Extinct (1907).

This plant was collected by W.H. Painter near Bishops Castle (SO3288) in 1896 and 1905 and at Ironbridge (SJ6703) in 1907. He named it *F. confusa* (= *F. bastardii*) but Pugsley decided that it was a separate taxon, possibly derived from a hybrid between *F. muralis* and *officinalis*. It has not been seen again.

Fumaria purpurea Pugsley
Purple Ramping-fumitory
Native. Scarce.

The first record of Purple Ramping-fumitory in Britain was by Johann Dillenius, who collected it 'ad sepes prope Shrewsbury' (in hedges near...) in 1726. The specimen is still in the herbarium at Oxford University, where it was identified by Herbert Pugsley in 1925 and was recently confirmed by John Burnett.

Leighton (1841) was aware that there was a distinctive fumitory in the vicinity of Shrewsbury, and he devotes most of p. 345 of his Flora to a description of it, concluding that 'it merits attention and further research.' What he describes seems to include both *F. muralis* and *F. purpurea*, which he observed 'about Shrewsbury generally' (SJ4912) and at Bayston Hill (SJ4808). Specimens of his at BM and DBN, collected in 1839, have subsequently been confirmed by Pugsley as *F. purpurea*, and one from Oswestry (SJ2929, 1840) at CGE has been named by P.D. Sell.

It was not until 1912 that Pugsley first described *Fumaria purpurea* as a distinct species, and he identified additional specimens by George Bentham (Acton Scott, SO4589, 1858), William Beckwith (Charlton Hill, SJ5807, 1882), George Claridge Druce (Stokesay Castle, SO4381, 1892), William Hunt Painter (Welshampton, 4334, 1910), Moyle Rogers (Shrewsbury, SJ4912, 1912) and James Cosmo Melvill (Meole Brace, SJ4810, 1912). Since then old specimens from Bishops Castle (SO3288, Painter, 1894), Pulverbatch (SJ4204, Richard Benson, 1894), Stapleton (SJ4605, Benson, 1902), Wilderley (SJ4301, Benson 1902) and Little Stretton (SO4491, Augustin Ley, 1909) have emerged (det. P.D. Sell and T.C.G. Rich).

In 1923 Norman Simpson found it still present at Stokesay Castle and in 1978 Helen Davidson reported it from Church Stretton (SO4593), although she failed to collect a voucher specimen, so that record could be considered unconfirmed.

In March 2000 we (Whild & Lockton) collected it at St. Mary's Water Lane in Shrewsbury (SJ4912), and in April that year at Condover (SJ4906) and Underdale (SJ5013). Maurice Hoare also found it at Ensdon (SJ4016) in April. All the recent records have been confirmed by Tim Rich. It seems quite likely now that *Fumaria purpurea* has been overlooked in recent times because the plants are what Pugsley described as var. *brevisepala* – an unusual form with shorter sepals, which appears to be largely confined to Shropshire. There is still a certain amount of taxonomic uncertainty about this species, which is considered to be endemic to the British Isles and the Channel Islands.

Fumaria purpurea

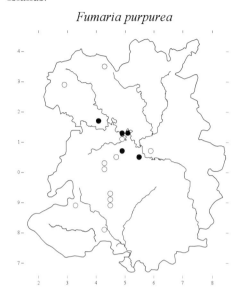

Gagea lutea (L.) Ker Gawl.
Yellow Star-of-Bethlehem
Native. Scarce.

Frances Pitt was the first to record this species in Shropshire, as recently as 1910. She was rather secretive about the locality, saying simply 'near Bridgnorth' (SO7192). Her site seems never to have been rediscovered, and it may have been in one of the extensive woodlands north of Bridgnorth, near to where Miss Pitt lived.

Two years later J.B. Duncan was shown it at Hampton Loade (SO7486) by A. Whitehouse of Dudley. It has evidently been known here ever since, but we have no more records for it there until 2004, when Mark Jannick reported it as very rare in two places in the dingle woodland above Hampton Loade (SO7585).

In April 1977 Ellen Heywood-Waddington found it by the Corn Brook near Whatmore (SO6171), where it has since been seen by Mary Fuller (1985), EHW again (1987 – 'still plentiful') and Jannick (2004). At the most recent count there were just 22 plants in a corner of a field, and it seems likely to be vulnerable at this site.

There are two distinct habitats for Yellow Star-of-Bethlehem. In the south of Britain it tends to grow near streams in damp woodlands, whereas in the north it occurs in dry woods and limestone pavements. In 1979 Doris Pugh found it in this latter habitat – on a wooded limestone outcrop at Craig-llwyn (SJ2327). It turns out that there are eight such sites for it in the squares SJ2326 & SJ2327, and in one of these there are over a thousand plants, growing in ancient W8 *Fraxinus excelsior* woodland (Dawes, Whild & Lockton, 2003). In other sites there are just a few plants, and they are vulnerable to grazing.

The most recently reported site in the county is Whithalls Wood (SO7484), back on the banks on the Severn, where Bob Kemp found it in 1981, and where it was most recently recorded by Ian & Jo Thompson in 2003.

Gagea lutea

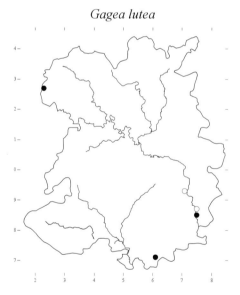

Galeopsis angustifolia Ehrh. ex Hoffm.
Red Hemp-nettle
Archaeophyte. Rare.

John Ray noticed Narrow-leaved All-heal, or Iron-wort, in fields of corn around Cambridge in 1660, and there is no doubt that it was once a common arable weed, particularly in the lowlands of the south-east of England, but it is possible that this species has a native ecology as well as its niche as an archaeophyte on cultivated land. Edward

Shiercliff listed it as one of the species to be found at St. Vincent's Rocks in the Avon Gorge in about 1689, and it has often been recorded on other limestone cliffs and screes around the British Isles since then.

In Shropshire *Galeopsis angustifolia* seems to have been largely restricted, historically, to the limestone areas around Wenlock Edge. Williams found it in 'ditch-banks, roadsides and cornfields' at Buildwas (SJ6304), Much Wenlock (SO6299) and 'Ledwich,' which could perhaps be Upper Ledwyche (SO5579), Lower Ledwyche (SO5374) or, most likely, Lutwyche (SO5594), all in about 1800. In Leighton's Flora of 1841 there are also records for Wenlock Edge by Francis Dickinson, Harriet Moseley, and by Leighton himself. Mary McGhie recorded it at Bromfield (SO4876) near the southern end of the Edge, which is slightly beyond its expected range but not impossible.

Thomas Bodenham found it in a field near Welbatch Coppice south of Shrewsbury (SJ4608), where there is some base-enrichment in the soil, to judge from other records for this site, and it was seen there again by William Beckwith in about 1882. Beckwith also made records for it along Wenlock Edge at about this time, at Presthope (SO5897), Kenley (SJ5600), and all around Much Wenlock, Little Wenlock (SJ6406) and the Wrekin (SJ6308). William Shoolbred collected it at Church Preen (SO5498) in 1872. In the early years of the 20th century George Potts and W.B. Allen recorded it around the northernmost parts of Wenlock Edge at Benthall (SJ6602), Wyke (SJ6402), Presthope (SO5897), and in fields near Edge Wood (SJ6101).

These records paint a picture of a species that occurs in disturbed soils along roadsides and in arable fields on the limestone. It is unlikely to have been truly native anywhere on Wenlock Edge although there are some areas of natural cliff and scree around Ippikin's Rock, near where Leighton saw it. In the arable fields it could well have been established for hundreds or even thousands of years.

The other place in Shropshire where it has been recorded, however, is intriguing. It turned up in some abundance at Jones's Rough nature reserve (SJ2424) in 1987, where it was found by C. Johnson in an area of natural limestone scree and low cliffs. It had been recorded in the vicinity as long ago as 1872, when Miss E. Jones collected it at the nearby Treflach Quarries (SJ2525), and it was subsequently noted by Ellen Lloyd at Porth-y-waen (SJ2523).

The current population of *Galeopsis angustifolia* in Shropshire is very small. About 100 plants have persisted in rubble in the yard of the British Telecom building in Llanymynech (SJ2621) for the last decade or so (Perring, 1992, Whild, 2004). The number at Jones's Rough had declined to about 20 plants in 2000, and on a roadside verge at Diddlebury (SO5086) there were a few plants in 1992, according to Mary Fuller.

Galeopsis angustifolia

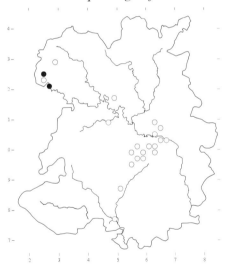

[*Galium pumilum* Murray]
Slender Bedstraw
Not in Shropshire.

Lloyd & Rutter (1957) state that this species is recorded on Titterstone Clee (SO5977) but give no details. Sinker (1985) changed this to *G. sterneri*, but then cast doubt on its veracity. By coincidence, a typographical error in 1990 resulted in John Bingham being wrongly credited with a record of it in the same place. There are, therefore, no good records of this species in the county.

Genista anglica L.

Petty Whin

Native. Rare.

This is a plant of moors, heaths and unimproved pasture in upland areas, and of the edges of bogs in the lowlands. It is still widespread in Britain, but the New Atlas shows a serious decline in the lowlands. Although it was once quite widespread, it is now known in just four sites in the county.

In 1726 Dillenius & Brewer recorded it in a boggy meadow at Norbury (SO3692). In about 1800 Williams found it in a pasture at Berrington (SJ5206), about the old coal-pits at Frodesley (SJ5102), on Harmer Moss (SJ4822), and at Pitchford Park (SJ5104). In 1817 Thomas Purton recorded it at Faintree (SO6688).

Leighton (1841) gives records for Bomere Pool (SJ4908, Leighton), Bridges (SO3996, Mansel), Caynton (SO6921, Bidwell), Shawbury Heath (SJ5420, Elsmere), 'the base of the Stiperstones Hill' (SO39 or SJ30, Dickinson), Tinkers Hill (SO5272, McGhie), Twyford Vownog (SJ3426, Dovaston), Whitcliffe (SO5074, Spare), and the 'borders of the Wyre Forest (SO77, Lees).

George Jorden recorded it 'towards the base of' Titterstone Clee (ca. SO57) in 1856. Griffith Griffiths (1870) recorded it on the Long Mynd (SO4293), but this is best considered unconfirmed. Phillips saw it at Bomere Pool again in 1878 and Beckwith refound it at Berrington and Shawbury Heath in the 1880s. He also found it in a small bog by Sharpstones Hill (SJ4909).

Sites for it since then include: Maesbury (SJ3025, Diamond, 1891), Bridges (H. Barnett, 1893), Ritton Castle (SO3497, Phillips, 1894), Kemberton (SJ7304, Painter, 1894), Llynaven (SO3076, T.R. Horton, 1900), Marrington (SO2796, Horwood, 1901), Shirlett Common (SO6598, Potts, 1901), Beggarhill Brook (SO6396, W.B. Allen, 1901), Cressage (SJ5904, G.A. Audley, 1902), Bridges again (Benson, 1904), Eaton-under-Heywood (SO4989, W.E. Thompson, 1904), Longville in the Dale (SO5494, Potts, 1907), and Welsh Frankton (SJ3633, O.M. Feilden, 1920).

In 1951 E.A. Wilson recorded it in a field opposite Ellesmere College (SJ4033), where it was seen by Ian Bonner in 1967 and by Pat Parker in 1983, but the site was planted with trees in 1985. Norah Mackenzie found it at Stapeley Hill (SO3200) in 1953, where Sinker also saw it in 1960, but the site was also later afforested.

It was first recorded at Shelve Pool (SO3397) by Frank Perring in 1975, and has since been seen by Chris Walker (1980-1990) and Kate Thorne (1990), but not since, despite several searches. Paul Bell found it at Betton Moss (SJ6836) in 1977, and has since recorded it in 1986, 1987 and 2001. Despite the site being partially drained, a few plants apparently still survive there.

In 1977 Ellen Heywood-Waddington found it at Catherton Common (SO6277), where John and Denise Bingham refound it in 2004. Joyce Warren discovered it at The Bog (SO3598) in 1977, where it has since been seen by Stokes (1994) and Whild & Lockton (1995), but it appears to have gone from there now.

There are four sites recorded by Will Prestwood for which we have no recent records: Marehay (SO3898, 1979), Cefn Gunthly (SO3394, 1979), Lubberland (SO6377, 1980) and Gorstley Rough (SO5974, 1982).

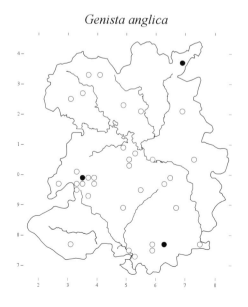

Genista anglica

Gentiana pneumonanthe L.

Marsh Gentian

Native. Rare.

This is arguably one of the most threatened species in Britain, having suffered a significant decline that is apparently continuing. Its only extant site in Shropshire is also the last remaining one in the whole Midlands region. This is Cramer Gutter Nature Reserve, an enclosed field on the edge of Catherton Common owned by the Shropshire Wildlife Trust (SO6479). It was first recorded here in 1962 by Sinker and Rutter, who were shown it by a certain Miss Aston. It is rather curious that it had been overlooked by George Jorden, who knew the area well in the 19th century, and it is possible that it is quite a recent arrival.

The only other site for this species in Shropshire was at Llanymynech (SJ2621), according to the label on an anonymous herbarium sheet at CGE with the date 1829.

At Cramer Gutter the Marsh Gentian appears to be in imminent danger of extinction. It occurs along the course of a flush that has been drying out completely in recent years. The field itself has become scrubbed over with gorse, and attempts to burn it off have only been partly successful.

Gentianella campestris (L.) Börner

Field Gentian

Native. Extinct (1986).

This is one of the most rapidly declining species in Britain, and it seems to be heading towards extinction in England, although it is still widespread in Scotland. It generally occurs in open grassland, usually on quite acidic soils.

Leighton listed four localities for it in 1841, all in limestone areas: Benthall Edge (SJ6603, Leighton), Wenlock Edge (SJ6100, T.C. Eyton), Limekiln Wood (SJ6509, Eyton), and Moelydd (SJ2425, Salwey, conf. Leighton). George Jorden listed it for Oreton (SO6580), Farlow (SO6480) and adjacent parts in 1856 – also on limestone.

Miss F.C. Benson first found it on the Stiperstones in 1892. This is more like its normal habitat – acidic soils and plenty of disturbed areas such as quarry waste. A Nature Conservancy Council surveyor found it there again in 1981, at The Napp (SO3599), where it was also seen by Chris Walker in 1985 and Pat Parker in 1986. At the nearby Pennerley Meadows (SO3599) it was also recorded by Walker in 1985 and Parker in 1986, but there are no records of it on the Stiperstones since then.

William Phillips found it still present at Oreton in 1895. W.B. Allen found it in the Wyre Forest (ca. SO7376) in 1905. James Cosmo Melvill discovered it at the foot of the Wrekin (SJ6308) in 1910 – possibly the same site as Eyton's Limekiln Wood.

In 1950 Norah Mackenzie refound it at Benthall Edge and she discovered a new site on Llynclys Hill (SJ2723) (another limestone hill) in 1972. She also saw it on Wenlock Edge. There are, however, no other good records since then, so the Pennerley sites are the only ones where it has been seen in the last 30 years, and it is nearly 20 years since it was last recorded there.

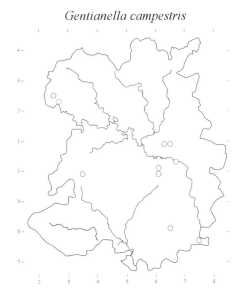

Gentianella campestris

Geranium rotundifolium L.

Round-leaved Crane's-bill

Neophyte. Rare.

Leighton (1841) was unimpressed with John Evans's record of this species as 'common about Shrewsbury' (SJ4912) in Turner &

Dillwyn's Botanist's Guide (1805). He searched diligently for it and even grew it in his garden at Luciefelde House (SJ4911) from seeds collected in Bath, but it became a troublesome pest there and was still present in the vicinity in 1973 (D.M. Evans & M.J. Connell) and 1976 (P.H. Oswald & Connell). It is a plant of track sides and hedge-banks on calcareous soils in the south of England, but it has expanded its range considerably in recent decades. In 2004 it was found by Sarah Whild in a hedgerow at Monkmoor Farm (SJ5214), where it was well established and not in close proximity to any gardens.

Geranium sanguineum L.
Bloody Crane's-bill
Native. Rare.

Although this species is widely introduced as a garden escape, there are a few native sites for it in the county. It is a plant of limestone rock exposures, and it was known in this situation by J.F.M. Dovaston on Llanymynech Hill (SJ2621) and Blodwel Rocks (SJ2623) in about 1841, but it has not been recorded there since.

George Jorden recorded it in the Wyre Forest (SO77) in about 1841, and it has also been recorded there by W.G. Perry (1841), Robert Garner (1844), William Beckwith (1882), Fred Fincher (1970, 1977) and John Bingham (1977, 1999). Malcolm Clark, who was coordinator for this area during Sinker's Flora project, always dismissed it as an introduction, but it is interesting to note that Sinker (1985) accepted it as a native there and, given the history of recording, that seems a reasonable conclusion.

The only other site with a reasonable claim to a native population of Geranium sanguineum is Earl's Hill (SJ4004), where it was found by Charles Sinker in 1958 and was last seen by Kate Thorne in 2002.

Geranium sylvaticum L.
Wood Crane's-bill
Native. Scarce.

Sinker argued that this species is native in certain woods in south Shropshire, and this is generally accepted, although it is not easy to decide precisely which populations are native and which are just garden escapes.

Edward Williams recorded it at Kinsley Wood (SO2872) in 1796 and in the hedge at Hopton Wafers Church (SO6376) at about the same time. It was still at Hopton Wafers in 1979 (Heywood-Waddington) and was abundant there in 1994 (Bingham). The Kinsley Wood site was arguably a native one.

Thomas Purton recorded it in Dudmaston Woods (ca. SO7488) in 1817. This could also have been a native site, as it is a plant of stream sides and damp woodlands. Mary McGhie found it on Titterstone Clee, near Bitterley (SO5777, 1841). She gives no details of the habitat, but many of her other records are of garden escapes.

George Jorden recorded it at 'Dowle Wood' in the Wyre Forest (SO7776) in about 1841. This is the first of many records for the Wyre, although the majority of them are for the Worcestershire side. It grows in clearings and along rides near the Dowles Brook and other streams in the forest at Wimperhill Wood (SO7476, Bingham, 1994), Longdon Wood (SO7576, Fincher, 1977 & SO7577, Bingham, 1994), Chamberline Wood (SO7676, Bingham, 1978) and Long Coppice (SO7579, Bingham, 1994).

The Reverend Waties Corbett recorded it in woods at Mawley Hall (SO6875) in 1841; Alfred Marston described it as 'scattered through most of the woods near Ludlow' (SO5175) in 1870; Thomas Diamond recorded it at Sweeny (SJ2725) in 1891; and Frances Pitt found it on a roadside at Linley (SO6898) in 1910. In 1950 E.A. Wilson recorded it on the verge of the Penley Road at Ellesmere (SJ3936).

In 1965 H.H. Shepherd recorded it at Tueshill Wood (SO3374). In 1975 Mary Fuller recorded it on a roadside verge at Clee St. Margaret, where it had been planted opposite a farm. In 1976 Joyce Roper found it in Hobarris Wood (SO3077), where it has since been seen by John Clayfield (1995 & 1997).

Ellen Heywood-Waddington found a single plant in a hedgerow at Haybridge (SO6473) in 1977; Audrey Ashwell recorded it at Old Rectory Wood (SO4493) in 1978; and Joyce

Roper found it at Pentre Hodre Pond (SO3276) in 1980, where it still was in 1996 (Whild). These are surely all introductions.

Geranium sylvaticum

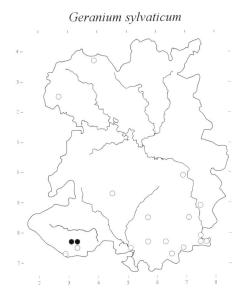

Two other possible native sites are Brineddin Wood (SO3176), where it was discovered by Roper in 1978 and has since been recorded by Bingham (1996) and Clayfield (1997); and Chorley Covert (SO7084), where Bill Thompson found it in 1981. The only thing we can say for sure about this species in Shropshire is that it grows in woodland edge habitat that is suitable for it. This does not seem to answer the question of whether and where it is native.

Gnaphalium sylvaticum L.
Heath Cudweed
Native. Scarce.

William Withering recorded this plant in a place called Sandy Heath (now Sandwood, SJ7706) near Shifnal in about 1787. This is probably the same site as Ruckley Heath, where George Lloyd recorded it in Leighton's Flora of 1841.

Edward Williams found it in a copse at Cound (SJ5505) and along sandy roads at Berrington (SJ5206) in about 1800. This is typical of the habitat in which it occurs: sandy, heathy woodland rides. Thomas Du Gard recorded it at Red Lake (SJ6810) in about 1840. Also in Leighton's Flora is a

record from Ludlow (SO5175) by Mary McGhie's of *G. sylvaticum* var. *fuscum*, with 'leaves woolly on both sides.' It seems unlikely that this was really *G. sylvaticum* at all.

Between 1878 and 1882 William Beckwith recorded it at High Rock, Bridgnorth (SO7293), on a hill near Stokesay (SO4381), and at Wenlock's Wood (SJ6307), Hawkstone Park (SJ5729) and Shawbury Heath (SJ5420). He also found it at the base of the Wrekin above Aston (SJ6208).

Richard Benson found it at Broom Hill (SJ4103) in 1892; W.E. Thompson recorded it at Smethcott (SO4599) in 1894 & 1895; E.B. Benson collected it at Stoke Heath (SJ6529) in 1895; and J.B. Johnson saw it at Quatford (SO7390) in 1939.

It has been recorded recently in just six sites in the county. At Hopton Titterhill (SO3577) it was seen by Rob Rowe in 1990 and John Clayfield in 1993. At Purvies Rough (SO7176) it was found by Malcolm Clark in 1976 but has not been seen since. At Wimperhill Wood (SO7476) it was recorded by John Bingham in 1991 and by Rob Stokes in 1995; and at nearby Longdon Orchard (SO7476) it was found by Bingham in 1998. Bingham also discovered it at Postenplain (SO7479) in 1998 and recorded it at Withybed Wood (SO7677) in 1978, 1986 and 1990.

Gnaphalium sylvaticum

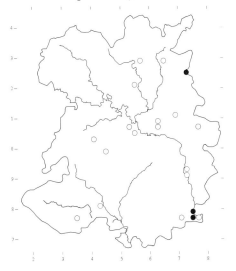

[*Groenlandia densa* (L.) Fourr.]
Opposite-leaved Pondweed
Not in Shropshire.

Although Edward Williams was generally reliable, his record (ca. 1800) of *Potamogeton densum* 'in ditches' should perhaps be treated with some caution. The only other record of it in the county was by Griffith Griffiths, who recorded it at Longnor (SJ4800) & Marshbrook (SO4489) in about 1870; but he is considered very unreliable.

Gymnadenia conopsea (L.) R.Br.
Fragrant Orchid
Native. Scarce.

The decline of this species in Shropshire has been very dramatic, and is not easy to explain. It is still a widespread species throughout the British Isles, but it is apparently decreasing everywhere, and especially so in the West Midlands region, where it is becoming very rare. It is a plant of dry limestone grasslands and wet calcareous fens, and it is currently split into three subspecies, which are quite distinct in both appearance and habitat. However, many recorders have not distinguished between them, and in Shropshire there are still no records of *G. conopsea* ssp. *conopsea*, despite a comment in Sinker's Flora that hints at its presence in the county.

Edward Williams was the first to record it in about 1800, at Cound Moor (SJ5502), Longner (SJ5211) and Pitchford (SJ5303). Thomas Purton found it at Bridgnorth (SO7192) in about 1817. Leighton (1841) gives eleven more sites, and describes it as a plant of upland limestone pastures. His records are for Benthall Edge (SJ6603, F. Dickinson), meadows near Coreley (SO6173, W. Corbett), Felton Moors (SO5076, M. McGhie), Hope Bagot (SO5874, McGhie), Oakly Park (SO4876, H. Spare), moors near Shortwood (SO5178, McGhie), Standhill Coppice (SJ6200, W.P. Brookes), under the Lawley (SO4999, Corbett), under the Long Mynd (SO4293, Corbett), Middlehope (SO4988, Leighton) and in the Wyre Forest (SO7576, Jorden).

In 1870 G.H. Griffiths recorded it in meadows near Enchmarsh (SO5096) and in 1880 Robert Serjeantson found it near Church Preen (SO5498). Beckwith recorded it at Spout Lane (SJ6306, 1880), Farley Dingle (SJ6302, 1880), Cressage (SJ5904, 1882) and Harley (SJ6000, 1882).

The first records for the limestone region in the north-west are given in Diamond's Flora of Oswestry, 1891. Here it is listed for Porth-y-waen (SJ2523) and Llanymynech (SJ2622). This region is where most of the remaining populations occur. It was first recorded on Llynclys Hill (SJ2723) by Ellen Lloyd in 1929 and has since been seen there by J.H. Owen (1945), Elizabeth Roberts (1989), Julie Clarke & Audrey Franks (1994), Whild & Lockton (1998) and Jackie Pedlow (1999). At Llanymynech rocks it has been recorded by Lloyd in 1929, Doris Pugh (1980, 1981 & 1982) and Celia Chaffey (1994 & 1997). In both sites it occurs in old abandoned quarries.

Other places for it in the north-west include Craignant (SJ2535, Lloyd, 1929), Craig Sychtyn (SJ2326, R.A. & A.P. Dawes, 2000), and Dolgoch Quarry (SJ2724, R.A. Dawes, 2004) – again, probably all quarries. At Sweeny Fen, however, it occurs in a different habitat: species-rich wet fen, best described as M22 *Juncus subnodulosus-Cirsium palustre* fen-meadow. It was first recorded here in 1969, possibly by Ian Bonner, who also saw it there in 1970. Since then it has been recorded by Doris Pugh (1979), John Packham & Ian Trueman (1979), Franklyn Perring (1989), Marjorie Wainwright (1991, 2000), Adrian Hillman *et al.* 1992), and Whild & Lockton (2000, 2004). The plants here are of the subspecies *densiflora* (Wahlenb.) E.G. Camus, Burgon & A. Camus (det. P.F. Hunt, 1980), as are those at Llanymynech Rocks.

In the areas around Wenlock Edge there were still sites for this species until at the 1920s. There are records for Sheinwood (SJ6102, William Phillips, 1891), The Vineyards (SJ6502, Potts, 1902), Shirlett (SO6597, Potts, 1902 & 1921), Easthope Wood (SO5695), Upper Millichope (SO5289), Middlehope (SO4988) & Westhope (SO4786) (all W. Beacall, 1904), Eaton-under-Heywood (SO4989), Upper Millichope and Ticklerton (SO4890) (all W.E. Thompson, 1904), Belswardyne (SJ6003, R.F.L. Burton, 1911), Longner (SJ521, Burton, 1920) and, finally, 'plentifully' at Homer (SJ6101) by George Potts in 1929.

Apart from the five current sites in the north-west of the county (probably all *densiflora*), there are two recent sites in the south-east, at Catherton Common (SO6277, A. Hearle, 1989) and in meadows at Bell Coppice (SO7175, M. Taylor, 1989; Bingham *et al.* 1998). These are considered to be ssp. *borealis* (Druce) F. Rose (det. Bingham). Records in Sinker's Flora for another part of the Wyre Forest (SO77N) and for the vicinity of Corndon Hill (SO29Y) may both be for sites outside the county.

Gymnadenia conopsea

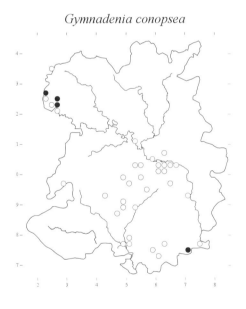

×*Gymnaglossum jacksonii* (Quirk) Rolfe
(*Gymnadenia conopsea* × *Coeloglossum viride*)
Native. Extinct (1920).

The Record of Bare Facts for 1923 reports that Mr R.F.L. Burton found this hybrid near Longner Hall (SJ5211) in 1920, and collected it to grow on. There are no subsequent records for the county.

Gymnocarpium robertianum (Hoffm.) Newman
Limestone Fern
Native. Extinct (1864).

Edward Lhwyd is said to have introduced this species at Llanforda (SJ2628) in the late 17th century, but it has not been recorded there since. William Whitwell recorded it on the bridge over the Morda at Oswestry (SJ2828) in 1864, but it was apparently taken by a florist. There have been several records since then, but they are probably all errors.

Griffith Griffiths recorded it at Cheney Longville (SO4284) in about 1870; Thomas Diamond (1891) lists it for Pen-y-llan (SJ2728), but without any explanation, and this record is not widely accepted. William Hunt Painter recorded it at Stoke Wood (SO4380) in 1908, in what was probably a mistake for Oak Fern *Gymnocarpium dryopteris*.

[*Helictotrichon pratense* (L.) Besser]
Meadow Oat-grass
Not in Shropshire.

It is quite a common mistake for visitors to Shropshire to record this species in the limestone areas but, as far as we can ascertain, it does not occur in the county.

Helleborus foetidus L.
Stinking Hellebore
Native. Scarce.

Although this species is widespread as a garden escape, it also occurs as a native plant in limestone areas. Its native habitat is in open woodland and on rock screes.

In Shropshire it was recorded by Edward Williams in 1800 as an introduction at Whittington Castle (SJ3231) and probably as a native plant in Farley Dingle (SJ6302). It was later seen at Whittington by Andrew Bloxam in about 1841, and at Farley Dingle by many recorders, including W.P. Brookes (1841), Beckwith (1880), George Potts (1902 & 1928), Winifred Hutton (1988), and Rob Stokes (2002).

Mary McGhie recorded it at Bitterley (SO5677) and Thomas Eyton found it at

Eyton (SJ4422) in about 1841. These were probably both introductions. George Jorden listed it for Oreton (SO6580), Farlow (SO6480) and 'adjacent parts.' It could have been native in that area, or perhaps it was associated with the quarries there.

In Diamond's Flora of Oswestry (1891) it is recorded at the Old Racecourse (SJ2631), Pant (SJ2722), Moelydd (SJ2425) and Rednal (SJ3628). Moelydd is the most convincingly native of these sites, and it has since been seen there by Doris Pugh in 1978, and at nearby Bwlch by Pugh & Wainwright in 1983 and at Jones's Rough by Whild & Lockton in 1999.

Richard Benson recorded it at The Oaks (SJ4204) in 1893 and Painter saw it at Hatton Grange (SJ7604) in 1897. Both of these were undoubtedly garden escapes, as was, probably, G.A. Audley's plant at Crickheath (SJ2922) in 1901.

Helleborus foetidus

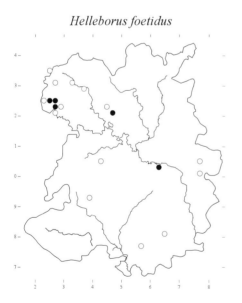

Doris Pugh was the first to record it on the limestone escarpment at Blodwel Rocks (SJ2623) in 1978. At the same time she recorded it at Treflach Quarry (SJ2625) and Whitehaven Quarry (SJ2624) and on Crickheath Hill (SJ2723). In the Flora of Montgomeryshire (1995) it is described as an introduction in this area, and it must be admitted that the records of it apparently in cultivation in the vicinity greatly pre-date any

suggestion of it being wild on Llanymynech & Llynclys hills. It tends to grow in old quarries and derelict gardens, such as at Black Bridge Quarry (SJ2724, J. Pedlow, 1989) and Treflach (SJ2624, J. Pedlow, 1991). Julie Clarke & Audrey Franks recorded it on the old railway line at Pant (SJ2722) in 1993.

If this species really is native in some sites in Shropshire, it seems that Moelydd and Farley Dingle are the most likely candidates. Elsewhere it occurs as a short-lived garden escape.

Hieracium cinderella (Ley) Ley

A Hawkweed

Native. Scarce.

This species is of local distribution in Britain, largely confined to the Welsh Marches; it could perhaps be described as Nationally Scarce, although the normal classification does not apply to critical taxa.

It was first recorded in Shropshire by William Hunt Painter at a wood near Bishops Castle (SO3288) in 1896 (conf. P.D. Sell, SHY). Painter also found it at Benthall Edge (SJ6603) and Cox Wood (SJ6604) in 1908. At Benthall Edge it was later recorded by Hildred Bigwood and Edward Rutter (det. Sell & West) in 1956; by Rob Stokes in 1997; and by Kate Thorne in 2001 (conf. D.J. McCosh).

Augustin Ley collected it at Marshbrook (SO4398) in 1909 (conf. Sell & West, CGE), where it has since been recorded by Helen Davidson (det. Sell) in 1979 and 1991, Joyce Warren in 1986, and Bill Thompson (conf. J. Bevan) in 1990. Ley also found it at Whitcliffe (SO5074, 1909, conf. Sell & West, CGE), on a roadside north of Knighton (SO2972, 1910, conf. Sell & West, CGE) and at Willey Park (SO6699, 1910, conf. Sell & West, CGE).

In 1910 William Hamilton collected it by the Habberley Brook at Earl's Hill (SJ4105, conf. Sell, SHY). Kate Thorne found it still there in 2002 (conf. McCosh).

In 1911 Melvill found it at Stoke Wood (SO4380, det. Sell & West, HWB).

No new sites were discovered until 1986, when Mary Fuller found it at Stoke St. Milborough (SO5682), where Bill Thompson also saw it in 1990 (conf. Bevan). Davidson and Thompson recorded it at Harton Hollow (SO4887) in 1990 (det. Bevan), where it was later collected by Whild & Lockton (2001, det. McCosh).

Bill Thompson made a tentative record of it in Withybed Wood (SO7576) in the Wyre Forest in 1990. This seems to be the first localised record for the Wyre, but there is also a dot for it there in the Critical Supplement (Perring & Walters 1968). More recently, Kate Thorne has found it at Snailbeach (SJ3702) and Farley Dingle (SJ6302) (both det. McCosh).

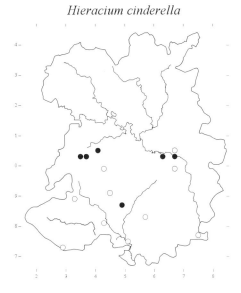

Hieracium cinderella

Hieracium lasiophyllum Koch
A Hawkweed
Native. Rare.

John Fraser discovered this species at Earl's Hill (SJ4104) in 1888 (det. W.H. Painter, HLU, LIVU, SHY), where it has subsequently been recorded by Hamilton (1903), Painter (1910), Sinker (1961), Fowler (1980), and most recently by Kate Thorne (2001, det. McCosh). It occurs on the cliffs and steep slopes on the eastern side of the hill, in U1 grassland.

In 1909 Ley discovered a second site, which he described as on 'rock at the head of Carding Mill Valley' (SO4395, det. P.D. Sell & C. West, CGE). This suggests the western, or upper end of the valley, whereas Kate Thorne's recent record of it by the Burway is towards the eastern end (SO4494, 2000, conf. D.J. McCosh).

Hieracium subcrassum (Almq. ex Dahlst.) Stenström
A Hawkweed
Neophyte. Rare.

Augustin Ley and Spencer Bickham collected this plant at Marshbrook (SO4490) in 1909 (det. P.D. Sell & C. West, B, CGE). Bill Thompson found it still there in 1990 (conf. Bevan, Sell & West). A second site was discovered by Thompson with Mary Fuller at Burnt House (SO5683) in 1987 (conf. Bevan), where it was last seen in 1990. It is considered to be an introduction in Britain.

Hippuris vulgaris L.
Mare's-tail
Native. Extinct (1897).

Edward Williams first recorded this species in the county in about 1800, in a ditch on Kynnersley Moor (SJ6716), where it was later seen by H. Bidwell (1841), R. Anslow (1865) and W. Phillips (1897). This was probably the only native site for it in the county, although it has been introduced at Marrington (SO2796, Horwood, 1901), Tickwood (SJ6402, Beckwith, 1882 & Allen, 1903), Willey Ponds (SO6698, Phillips, 1893; Kingham, 1978 & Paskell, 1982) and Moreton Hall (SJ2935, Wainwright, 1982). It occurs in calcareous waters throughout Britain, but is absent from the acid rock catchments in western regions.

Hordelymus europaeus (L.) Jessen
Wood Barley
Native. Scarce.

This is considered an ancient woodland indicator in Shropshire, occurring only in W8 woodland along Wenlock Edge and in the Oswestry uplands. It was first recorded by Painter at Benthall Edge (SJ6503) in 1895, and it has been recorded there subsequently by Chris Walker (1977), Ian Trueman (1981), John Box (1985-1995), Rob Stokes (1996) and Sarah Whild (2003). It is not abundant there, but there are many clumps scattered throughout the wood.

In 1976 Walker found it at Edge Wood (SJ6100) and at Longville Coppice (SO5493). Ian Bolt added Loamhole Dingle (SJ6605) to the list of sites in 1977, and Walker found it further up the valley at Lydebrook Dingle (SJ6506) in 1980. In 1982 Kate Thorne discovered it at Blodwel Rocks (SJ2622, conf. Whild) – the only time it has been recorded on the Carboniferous Limestone in north-west of the county. That year P.M. Stocks reported it at Thatcher's Wood (SO7090).

Trueman first recorded it at Harton Hollow (SO4887) in 1994, where it has subsequently been seen by Roy Perry & Mark Lawley in 1995 and by Sarah Whild in 2001. Two other sites for it have been discovered recently: Preenshead Wood (SJ6902, Lockton, 1997) and Betchcott Hollow (SO4498, Prestwood, 1998).

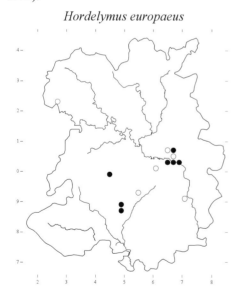

Hordelymus europaeus

Hordeum secalinum Schreber
Meadow Barley
Native. Extinct (1978).

This is a common species on heavy clay soils in the south-east of Britain, but Shropshire is just outside its range. Edward Williams recorded it at Sundorne (SJ5215) and at Battlefield Church (SJ5117) in about 1800. Edward Elsmere collected it at New Park, Shrewsbury (SJ4913, conf. Leighton) in 1841, where William Phillips also saw it in 1878. Henry Spare reported it at Oakly Park (SO4876, 1841). It was found by Winifred Hutton in rough grassland by the River Worfe at Stableford (SO7599 & SO7699) in 1978, but that site was ploughed shortly afterwards.

In 2000 Dave Buckingham recorded it at Wollaston (SJ3212), but did not collect a voucher specimen, so his record is considered unconfirmed.

Hornungia petraea (L.) Rchb.
Hutchinsia
Native. Extinct (1855).

The only records of this species in the county are by Thomas Salwey, who recorded it at Pentregaer (SJ2328), Trefonen (SJ2526) and 'on hills facing Llansilin' – presumably Craig-llwyn (SJ2228) in 1855.

Huperzia selago (L.) Bernh. ex Schrank & Mart.
Fir Clubmoss
Native. Rare.

Edward Williams found this species in about 1800 on all three of the highest hills in Shropshire: Brown Clee (SO5986), Titterstone Clee (SO5977) and the Stiperstones (SO3698). Leighton added Caer Caradoc (SO4795) to the list in 1877, and Diamond recorded it at Craig-y-rhiw (SJ2329) in 1891. Griffith Griffiths claimed to have seen it on the Long Mynd (SO4293) in about 1870, but like many of his records this seems very unlikely. The only other place it has been found was on a spoil heap from an opencast coal mine at Stoneyhill in Telford (SJ6606, Whild, 1983), but it was destroyed during the construction of the adjacent landfill site.

It is only at Titterstone Clee that Fir Clubmoss has ever been seen again. George Jorden saw it there in about 1856; Chris Walker & Will Prestwood refound it in 1977; Pat Parker mapped its distribution there in 1986; and it has been recorded several times since, most recently by Bingham & Whild in

2002. It grows in deep crevices in the boulder scree along the north side of the summit, where it is protected from the weather and from sheep grazing. A number of other rare ferns occur in the same habitat.

Hymenophyllum wilsonii Hook.
Wilson's Filmy-fern
Native. Extinct (1984).

Shropshire is on the eastern edge of the range for this species, and the climate here is generally too dry. It has probably only been recorded in two sites. Leighton collected a specimen at Treflach Wood (SJ2624) in 1840 (SHY), where it was seen by Salwey in 1855, and by Emily Farmer in 1864 (LUD).

On the Long Mynd, J.F. Crouch first found it at Light Spout Hollow (SO4394) in 1877. William Phillips collected a specimen there, too (undated – some time before 1905). John Packham then discovered it in the nearby New Pool Hollow (SO4394) in 1975 (conf. A.C. Jermy, BM), where it lasted at least until 1984, but it has not been seen since, despite many searches.

Hypericum linariifolium Vahl
Toadflax-leaved St. John's-wort
Neophyte. Extinct (1919).

There is only one record for Shropshire, best described by these extracts from the original publications.

In the Record of Bare Facts for 1919: 'Division XII. In extremely small quantity, but unmistakably this rare species. It is the rarest of our native St. John's Worts and restricted to the Southern Counties and Channel Isles. We can hardly imagine it anything but a casual here. It was discovered by Mr W.B. Allen, who was kind enough on 27th June last, to conduct me to the place where I beheld it 'in situ.' Our joint diagnosis was confirmed by Mr Edmund G. Baker, of the Botanical Department, British Museum. For various reasons, the exact locality is not given.'

In the Botanical Exchange Club Report for 1923: 'as an adventive near Buildwas, Salop. W.B. Allen & J.C. Melvill.'

Whether this amounts to two records – one in 1919 and one in 1923 – is not clear. Sinker (1985) described the locality as 'near Bridgnorth,' but this was presumably an educated guess based on the botanical division. Buildwas (SJ6304) is in Division 11, not 12, so Allen & Melvill may have been deliberately misleading.

Hypericum montanum L.
Pale St. John's-wort
Native. Rare.

There have been few records of this species in Shropshire since the 1980s, and recent searches for it have been unsuccessful, but it seems too soon to declare it extinct in the county. The reason for its decline is unknown. It is a plant of limestone areas, occurring in hedgerows, grassland and scrub.

The first record was by Littleton Brown in 1725, 'between Corfton and Munslow' (SO4985), which is on the east side of Wenlock Edge. Leighton (1841) gives just five records, two of which he confirmed from specimens. These were collected by Salwey 'above Wolverton on Wenlock Edge' (SO4787) and by W.P. Brookes at Standhill Coppice (SJ6200). The other three were by Mary McGhie, who claimed to have seen it at Ashford (SO5271), Ludford (SO5173) and Steventon (SO5273), but these records should be treated with some caution.

Robert Garner (1844) listed it for the Wyre Forest, without specifying which county. Thomas Salwey was the first to discover it in the north-west of Shropshire, at Treflach (SJ2525) in 1855. Griffith Griffiths's record for Marshbrook (SO4489) in 1870 seems quite unlikely.

William Beckwith was a careful botanist, and his records for Stoke Wood (SO4281, 1878) and Easthope (SO5695, 1889) are entirely credible. William Hunt Painter found it at Sutton Maddock (SJ7201) in 1894. This was presumably on a road side, as was the plant that William Phillips saw at Hockleton (SJ2700) in 1899. W.E. Thompson described it as sparse on Wenlock Edge above Eaton-under-Heywood Church (SO5998) in 1904.

Miss M.H. Bigwood recorded it at Chorley (SO6983) in 1953 and 1962. Edward Rutter recorded it on Llynclys Hill (SJ2723) in 1954, and it was subsequently seen on the nearby Blodwel Rocks (SJ2623) by Doris Pugh in 1978, and on Llynclys Hill again by Jackie Pedlow and Marjorie Wainwright in 1996. Pugh also saw it at Whitehaven Quarry (SJ2624) in 1975 & 1978; at Bryn Celyn (SJ2525) in 1978, where it was still present in 1987 (R.A. Dawes conf. Wainwright); and at Treflach Wood (SJ2525) in 1983.

Bill Thompson found it on the sidings of the Severn Valley Railway at Hampton Loade (SO7486) in 1981, and Ellen Heywood-Waddington recorded it near a quarry at Knowle Hill (SO6981) the same year. Bert Webster recorded it 'growing wild' in his garden at Pant (SJ2621) in 1983 and at the nearby Llanymynech Heritage Area in 1993. In 1987 Ruth Dawes recorded it at Treflach (SJ2624), and in 1993 Frank Perring had it in both Jones's Rough (SJ2424) and in an adjacent field.

The only current dot on the map, therefore, is for Llynclys Hill, where Jackie Pedlow & Marjorie Wainwright recorded it 'being eaten by insects before flowering' in 1996.

Hypericum montanum

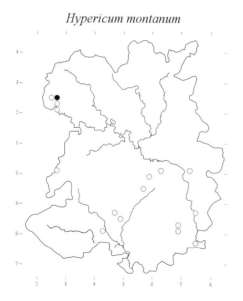

Hypochaeris glabra L.
Smooth Cat's-ear
Native. Rare.

Edward Williams recorded this species in five places in the county in about 1800: Eaton Mascott (SJ5305), Harmer Hill (SJ4922), Knockin Heath (SJ3521), Sundorne (SJ5215) and on the Wrekin (SJ6308). Edwin Lees found it on a roadside bank at Dawley (SJ6907) in about 1835. Leighton recorded it at Earl's Hill (SJ4004) and Hopton Hill (SJ3820) in 1841.

Phillips found it still present at Sundorne in 1878; and William Moyle Rogers saw it at The Cliffe (SJ3920) near Hopton Hill in 1894. In 1904 R.M. Barrington collected it at Church Stretton (ca. SO4593). Painter found it at Highley (SO7483) in 1907 and at Apley Park (SO7198) the following year.

Edward Rutter found it in a sand quarry at Cound Arbour (SJ5505) in 1956, and in 1962 Sinker refound it at Earl's Hill. It grew on stabilised scree on the east side of the hill, but it has not been seen there since 1966 (Sinker & Perring).

Bryan Fowler found two plants at White Ladies Priory (SJ8207) in 1976, but they were gone by 1986. Sarah Stafford also reported it from Loton Park (SJ3613) in 1976, but again it has not been seen there since.

The only recent record is by Kate Thorne, who found it at Boreton Bank (SJ5107) in 1990.

Impatiens noli-tangere L.
Touch-me-not Balsam
Native. Rare.

The first British record of this species was at Marrington Dingle (SO2797) by George Bowles in 1632, and it has since been recorded there many times, most recently by Rob Mileto in 2002. In 1991 P.E. Hatcher attempted to define the native sites for this species by association with the Netted Carpet Moth *Eustroma reticulata*, the larvae of which feed exclusively on Touch-me-not Balsam. Although the moth was not found at

Marrington Dingle, the population there is still widely accepted as truly native.

Elsewhere in the county it has been recorded as an introduction, at Mainstone (SO2787) by R.C. Palmer in 1951, by Joyce Warren in 1981 & 1985 and by Joyce Roper in 1986; Badger Dingle (SO7799) by Melvill in 1913 & 1914 and by Winifred Hutton in 1974 & 1977; Acton Burnell (SJ5302, Serjeantson, 1881); Eyton on the Weald Moors (SJ6514, Painter, 1908); Welsh Frankton (SJ3632, Diamond, 1891 & Feilden 1920); Hardwick (SJ3734, Feilden, 1921); and Rindleford (SO7395, M.H. Bigwood, 1953).

Impatiens noli-tangere

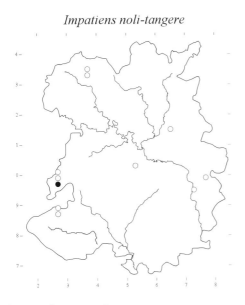

Isoetes lacustris L.
Quillwort
Native. Extinct (1893).

Edward Williams first found this species at Bomere Pool (SJ5007) in about 1798, where it was subsequently recorded by William Phillips in 1874 and Thomas Butler in 1880. There is also an anonymous specimen at Shrewsbury Museum dated 1893. Sinker's comment that it survived there until the 1950s appears to be unsubstantiated, but it seems entirely possible. William Beckwith collected it at The Mere, Ellesmere (SJ4034) in 1883. These are the only sites in Shropshire where it has been found, as Griffith Griffiths's record for Darnford (SO4297) is very dubious. It is an indicator of unpolluted clear

water, and was probably present in the county as a glacial relic.

Juncus compressus Jacq.
Round-fruited Rush
Native. Extinct (1924).

Andrew Bloxam discovered this plant in the floodplain of the Severn near Bridgnorth (SO7192) in 1841. It was subsequently seen there by Hamilton in 1900 and by Druce in 1924, but not since then. Although this is the native habitat for it, it would be on the western edge of its range in Shropshire.

Juncus subnodulosus Schrank
Blunt-flowered Rush
Native. Scarce.

J.E. Bowman described this species as 'more or less abundant on the margins of most of the meres near Ellesmere' in 1841, but he specifically recorded it only near the lime kiln at Cole Mere (SJ4333). This is quite revealing, as Blunt-flowered Rush has been declining in Shropshire in recent years for no apparent reason. It grows in calcareous fens, and it is possible that it was once more common as a result of the processing and application of lime.

At Cole Mere it was last recorded in 1882 by William Beckwith, who also found it at Crose Mere (SJ4230), where it still occurs in reasonable abundance (Whild & Lockton, 2003). Beckwith also found it at Fenemere (SJ4422), where Francis Rose and Charles Sinker saw it in 1959 and 1970 respectively. It still occurs at The Yesters (SJ4422), which is part of the same peat basin, where it was found by Sinker in 1965 and has since been recorded often, most recently by Rob Mileto in 1996.

The only other mere for which there are records is Morton Pool (SJ3023), where it was first recorded by Chris Walker and Martin Wigginton in 1981. It was not in the vicinity of the mere itself, but in damp grassland adjacent to the long-abandoned lime kiln that stood by the Montgomery Canal. The grassland has gradually dried out and become more acidic in nature, and the *J. subnodulosus* was last seen there in 1993 by Andrew Hearle. The landscaped pool at Aston Hall (SJ3227) is arguably a 'mere,' and Doris Pugh recorded it there in 1978.

Sometimes it occurs in or close to canals and railway lines, possibly due to the influence of base-rich clay and limestone chippings. At Aston Locks (SJ3326) it was found by Whild & Lansdown in 1997, and was still there in 2003 (Newbold). Beckwith, in 1880, recorded it by the Shrewsbury Canal at Berwick Wharf (SJ5411). It also used to grow alongside the railway line in Llynclys (SJ2724, Pugh, 1976 & Wainwright, 1988) and at Porth-y-waen (SJ2623, Pugh, 1979).

There is a smattering of recent records from agricultural sites, including Tycoch Farm (SJ2823, Pugh, 1979), Fernhill (SJ3232, Walker, 1986), Nantmawr (SJ2524, G.M. Stone, 1996 & R. Mileto, 1999), Millenheath (SJ5734, Whild, 1994 & Stone, 1996) and a ditch at Stanwardine in the Fields (SJ4224, Parker, 1996). It is also abundant on Shropshire Wildlife Trust's reserve at Sweeny Fen (SJ2725), where it was first recorded by Ian Bonner in 1969, and where it is considered to be invasive and rather troublesome.

The only other site for which there are recent records is Dolgoch Quarry (SJ2724), where it was found by Walker in 1988 and was still present in 1998 (Whild & Lockton).

Juncus subnodulosus

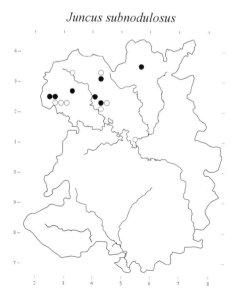

Juniperus communis L.
Juniper
Native. Extinct (1891).

Juniper is presumably a glacial relic in Shropshire, which survived in a few places in the county until historical times. Leighton did not record it himself in his flora of 1841, but he cited records by Mary McGhie for woods near Burford (SO5868), Ashford Carbonel (SO5270) and Ludlow (SO5174). Several of McGhie's other records are suspect, and these should not necessarily be assumed to be correct, although it is not a difficult plant to identify.

Leighton also gave a record by George Jorden for Kingswood (SO7377) in the Wyre Forest, where Jorden described it as 'truly wild.' W.G. Perry also recorded it in the Wyre Forest at about the same time, and Jorden added Furnace Coppice (SO7176) and Sturt Common (SO7277) in 1856. There is also an undated specimen at SHY collected by Leighton in the Wyre Forest.

In 1891 Diamond listed it for Carreg-y-big (SJ2532) and Craignant (SJ2535) in his Flora of Oswestry – possibly based on records by O.M. Feilden.

Lathyrus aphaca L.
Yellow Vetchling
Neophyte. Extinct (1980).

There are just two records of this species in the county. Doris Pugh found it by the telephone kiosk in Pant (SJ2722) in 1963, and K.E. Daniels reported it at Poles Coppice (SJ3904) in 1980, but it has not been seen in either location again.

Lathyrus nissolia L.
Grass Vetchling
Neophyte. Rare.

William Phillips apparently collected a specimen of this plant at an unspecified location 'in the west of the county' in about 1905. It was not recorded again until 1985, when John Box & J. Mincher recorded it at Randlay (SJ7107) and Stirchley Grange (SJ7007). Phillip & Sylvia Kingsbury found it on a roadside at Hodnet (SJ6129) in 1991, and Rob Stokes recorded it at Donnington (SJ7014) in 1994. It is considered to be a native plant of disturbed soils in the south of Britain, and it has been spreading northwards in recent years. In 2004 Fiona Gomersall and Tess Pearson discovered it in farmland near Llanfair Waterdine (SO2480), close to a track but not obviously introduced.

Lathyrus sylvestris L.
Narrow-leaved Everlasting-pea
Native. Rare.

Although there is speculation that this species is just a casual inland (Pearman in New Atlas, p. 387), it does seem to have been along the banks of the Severn in the vicinity of Shrewsbury for a very long time.

It was first recorded by Babington & Leighton on the river bank and by the adjacent canal between Shrewsbury and Uffington (SJ5114) in 1832. This may be where Norah Mackenzie saw it 'near Ditherington' in 1955 and where Jennifer Roberts recorded it again in 1975.

Other sites by the Severn near Shrewsbury include Shelton Rough (SJ4614) by Leighton (1841), Phillips (1878), Beckwith (1889), G.E. Johnson (1910) and S.R. Turner (1972, 1980 & 1987); Eaton Constantine (SJ5905, Beckwith, 1880); Preston Boats (SJ5212, Leighton, 1841); Preston Montford (SJ4314, Sinker, 1965); Castlefields (SJ5012, Roberts, 1975); and The Mount, Shrewsbury (SJ4713) by Turner (1963) and Helen Matthews (1976 & 1977). In 1992 Gill Castle & Rob Mileto found it on the edge of woodland overlooking the Old River Bed in Shrewsbury (SJ4914), where it still was in 1995 (Whild & Lockton).

Elsewhere in Shropshire it seems to be a casual of roadsides and railway tracks. The records are for Caus Castle (SJ3307, Dickinson, 1841), Hucksbarn (SO5072, Salwey, 1841), along the road between Ludlow and Tenbury (SO5374, Salwey, 1841), Ludlow (SO5175, McGhie, 1841), a wood near Acton Scott (SO4589, Griffiths, 1870), Evenwood (SJ5501, Beckwith, 1880), Wyre Forest (SO7576, Rutter, 1954), Pant Railway Station (SJ2722, Pugh, 1964-1978), Diddlebury Common (SO4786, A. Dyer,

1970), a hedge in Pant (SJ2722, Pugh, 1970 & 1978), and a road verge at Hilton (SO7795, Stokes, 1995).

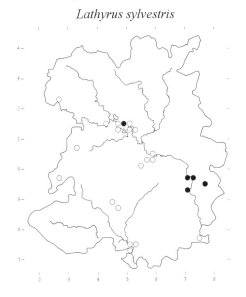

Lathyrus sylvestris

Legousia hybrida (L.) Delarbre
Venus's-looking-glass
Archaeophyte. Rare.

Shropshire is somewhat beyond the range of this arable weed, and it has always been rare here. Edward Williams recorded it in corn fields on his estate at Eaton Mascott (SJ5305) in about 1800. Waties Corbett found it in corn fields at Nash Court (SO6071) in 1841, and William Penny Brookes recorded it in fields near Windmill Hill in Much Wenlock (SJ6200) at about the same time.

Later records include Church Stretton (SO4593, Griffiths, 1870), Benthall (SJ6602, Painter, 1901), Buildwas (SJ6302, Anon., ca. 1913), and Morville (SO6694, F. Pitt, 1914). Most of the more recent records are from the Wenlock Edge. George Potts found it in a field above Edge Wood (SJ6101) in 1929; Edward Rutter recorded it in a field near Stretton Westwood (SO5998) in 1955 and at Easthope (SO5695) in 1961; and John Swindells & Sarah Whild found it in a field above Blakeway Hollow (SO6099) in 2000. It presumably comes up from buried seed and flourishes for a short while, so the chance of it being spotted by a botanist during that time seem slight. Dave Buckingham found a single plant in the yard at Brockhurst Farm, Wem (SJ5428) in 2000 (conf. Whild).

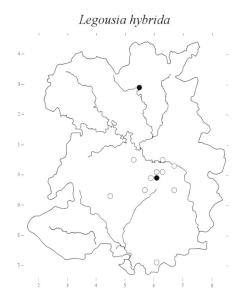

Legousia hybrida

Lepidium latifolium L.
Dittander
Neophyte. Extinct (1993).

Although it is considered native in some parts of Britain, this species only occurs as a casual in Shropshire. Will Prestwood found it by the River Onny at Craven Arms (SO4382) in 1989; and Elizabeth Roberts and Emily Townsend found it on pavements in Oswestry (SJ2829 & SJ2929) in 1993.

Lepidium ruderale L.
Narrow-leaved Pepperwort
Neophyte. Rare.

This plant is listed as an archaeophyte in the New Atlas. In Shropshire it appears generally to be a rare casual. Richard Benson first recorded it at Vale Castle (SJ5729) in 1904. George Potts found it in a chicken run at Benthall (SJ6602) in 1919. Elizabeth Roberts found it growing in a pavement in Oswestry (SJ2829) in 1989 (conf. P.M. Benoit). Sarah Whild collected it on the side of the road at Shelton (SJ4613) in 1997 (conf. F.H. Perring), where it still occurs (Whild, 2004). Rob Stokes found it in a car park at Coton Hill (SJ4913, conf. Whild) in 2001.

Limosella aquatica L.
Mudwort
Native. Extinct (1962).

Although it is locally frequent on the muddy margins of the Severn in Montgomeryshire (Trueman, Morton & Wainwright 1995), this species seems only to occur sporadically in Shropshire. Leighton recorded it on 'sandy, muddy margins of the Severn' at Shelton Rough (SJ4614) in 1841, and Phillips repeated his record verbatim in 1878. Beckwith found it in a pool on Charlton Hill (SJ5807) in 1880. Edward Rutter found it by the Severn at Preston Montford (SJ4314) in 1962, but it has not been seen in the county since then.

Listera cordata (L.) R.Br.
Lesser Twayblade
Native. Extinct (1920).

Shropshire is rather beyond the range of this northerly, upland species, but it apparently did survive in the county until the recent past. Littleton Brown recorded it on the Stiperstones (SO3699) in 1726, and Leighton found it still there in 1841. Diamond listed it for Craignant (SJ2535) in 1891, but that does seem a rather dubious record. Oswald Feilden claimed to have found it at Welshampton (SJ4334) in 1892, and reported it again in 1920; but he was rather secretive of the precise locality, which might have been Clarepool Moss.

Lithospermum arvense L.
Field Gromwell
Archaeophyte. Extinct (1986).

Shropshire was once well within the range of this arable weed, but it has retreated to the south-east of England, and several of the recent records of it in the county are from roadsides.

Edward Williams listed it as common in 1800 but gave no specific localities. Joseph Babington also considered it common in corn fields near Ludlow (SO5174) in 1803, and commented that he had seen it on the town walls.

In Leighton's Flora of 1841 it is recorded at Eyton (SJ4422, T.C. Eyton), Hadnall (SJ5220, W.W. Watkins), Ludlow (H. Spare), Oswestry (SJ2929, Salwey), and Welbatch (SJ4508, Bodenham, conf. Leighton). It was still at Welbatch when Phillips recorded it there in 1878.

Beckwith (1880) found it at Garmston (SJ6006) and Hardwick (SJ3734); Richard Benson collected it at Pulverbatch (SJ4202) in 1894; and George Potts and William Allen found it near Buildwas Station (SJ6404) in 1904.

In 1974 Henry Hand found it on a roadside at Ackleton (SO7698). Bryan Fowler found it in the corner of an arable field at Hinton (SJ4008) in 1980. In 1986 Winifred Hutton reported two plants at Bridal Coppice (SO7692).

Lithospermum arvense

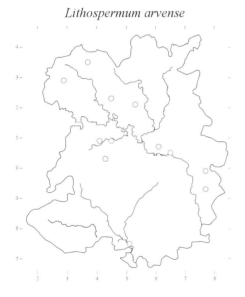

Littorella uniflora (L.) Asch.
Shoreweed
Native. Scarce.

This is a common plant in the north and west of Britain, but in Shropshire it has always been rare and it is an important ecological indicator for unpolluted and unspoiled habitats. It grows on the margins of lakes and pools with low nutrient status and naturally fluctuating water levels. Until recently it was only known in the meres. Edward Williams recorded it at Bomere Pool (SJ4908), Betton Pool (SJ5107), Crose Mere (SJ4230), White

Mere (SJ4132) and in a pool on Perthy Common, which could be what is now called Hardwick Pool (SJ3733), all in about 1800. Bloxam and Leighton both saw it at The Mere, Ellesmere (SJ4034) in about 1841, and Leighton also recorded it at Cole Mere (SJ4333) and on the east shore of Bomere Pool (SJ5007).

It was still present at Bomere and Betton pools when Phillips surveyed in 1874; and at Bomere and Ellesmere when Beckwith visited in 1882. In 1891 Diamond listed it for The Mere, Ellesmere and White Mere (SJ4132). It 1894 it was recorded in Blake Mere (SJ4133) and in the Llangollen Canal at Ellesmere (SJ4034) by the 'Midland Union' – possibly J.W. Heath.

In 1903 it was recorded for the first time in an upland situation, at Bettws-y-Crwyn (SO2081, J.A. Panter), at an altitude of about 390m. There were then no more records until 1962 when G.P. Richards found it by the River Teme at Nether Skyborry (SO2773) – the only time it has been recorded in a river in this county.

Littorella uniflora

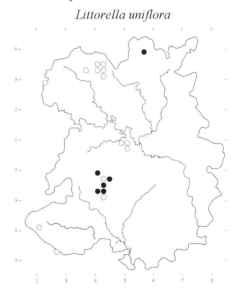

In 1972 and 1975 Frank Perring discovered it in two more lowland meres – Brown Moss (SJ5639) and Llyn Rhuddwyn (SJ2328) – and in 1979 Martin Wigginton found it at White Mere and Newton Mere (SJ4234). It is interesting to note that all the meres in which it had been recorded previously had stabilised water levels by this time, whereas the ones where it persisted were still in a more natural state.

In 1979 Joyce Roper made the first record for the Long Mynd, in a flush above Ashes Hollow (SO4293, conf. Sinker). Since then it has been recorded in numerous places on the Long Mynd, and is has become so common there that it can no longer be considered a Shropshire rarity. Specific localities include Middlehill Pool (John Bingham, SO4291, 1984), Wild Moor (SO4296, Janet Lister, 1985 & 1990), Pole Cottage Pools (SO4193, Philip & Sylvia Kingsbury, 1990; Kate Thorne 1999), Callow Hollow (SJ4193, Thorne, 1999), Thresholds (SO4198, Thorne, 1999), Gogbatch (SO4596, Thorne, 2000), The Batch (SO4395, Mags Cousins, 2001) and Carding Mill Valley (SO4393, Cousins, 2001).

At Llyn Rhuddwyn it was been recorded by Trueman in 1984 and Walker in 1986, but we have no records of it there since then. It still occurs in some abundance around the main pool at Brown Moss (Lockton & Whild, 2004).

Lobelia dortmanna L.
Water Lobelia
Native. Extinct (1922).

The presence of *Lobelia dortmanna* in the Shropshire meres until recent times demonstrates how oligotrophic these water bodies must have been. In England this plant has only ever been found in Cumbria and Shropshire, although it is widespread in western parts of Scotland, Ireland and Wales.

The first record for the county was probably by Edward Williams at White Mere (SJ4132) in about 1800, although John Evans also found it at Bomere Pool (SJ4908) in about 1805. It has not been seen at White Mere again, but it was subsequently recorded at Bomere Pool by Leighton (1841), Phillips (1874) and Beckwith (1880). Andrew Bloxam recorded it at Blake Mere (SJ4133) in 1841, and it has since been there seen by Beckwith (1880), Diamond (1891) and Feilden (1920). At Berrington Pool (SJ5207) it was recorded by Leighton (1841), Phillips

(1878), Beckwith (1880) & Hamilton (1893). The only other mere for which there is a record is Newton Mere (SJ4234, Beckwith, 1880).

There are two rather curious records for this species in upland locations. Waties Corbett recorded it in pools on the Long Mynd (ca. SO4293) in 1841, and G.M. Furley recorded it in small pools on the Stiperstones range (ca. SO3698) in 1922. That it should have been overlooked in both of these well-known localities by so many botanists is strange, and perhaps both of those records should be treated with some caution.

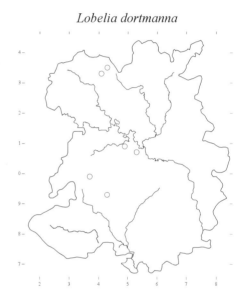

Lobelia dortmanna

Lolium temulentum L.
Darnel
Archaeophyte. Extinct (1891).

This species was once a serious agricultural pest in lowland England, but Shropshire appears to have been on the very edge of its range. In 1799 Edward Williams recorded it at Eaton Mascott (SJ5305) and Shawbury Heath (SJ5420). Leighton (1841) gives records for Welbatch (SJ4508, Bodenham), Hadnall (SJ5220, Elsmere), Ludlow (SO5175, McGhie) and Hucksbarn (SO5072, Salwey). In 1856 Jorden recorded it at Oreton, Farlow and adjacent parts (SO6580). The last record for the county is in Diamond's Flora of 1891, for the Oswestry area (ca. SJ2929).

Lotus glaber Mill.
Narrow-leaved Bird's-foot-trefoil
Neophyte. Rare.

There are only four records for this species in the county. O.M. Feilden first recorded it at Welsh Frankton (SJ3633) in 1920; G.P. Richards apparently found it near Kinsley Wood (SO2872) in the 1960s; and Pat Parker recorded it on a roadside verge at Stanwardine (SJ4025) in 1991 and 1996. It is primarily a plant of waste ground in the south-east of England, especially around the coast.

Luronium natans (L.) Raf.
Floating Water-plantain
Native. Rare.

A good case can be made for *Luronium natans* to be Britain's most important plant, from the point of view of nature conservation. It is rare and threatened globally, being restricted to north-western Europe and in decline throughout its range. It is also a good habitat indicator, growing in clear, unpolluted waters. It seems likely that it colonised Britain at a respectable distance behind the retreating ice sheet, as it cannot tolerate a very cold climate. The numerous lakes, rivers and mires of the Shropshire plain must have suited it perfectly, and it may have occurred in most of them at some point. Edward Williams was among the first to record it, at Sundorne Pool (SJ5215), Hencott Pool (SJ4916), Blake Mere (SJ4133), Ebreywood (SJ5417), Shawbury (SJ5420), Shawbury Heath, White Mere (SJ4132) and in the River Roden (SJ4729). Some of these records are dated 1796, when Arthur Aikin also recorded it at Hencott Pool.

Joseph Babington noted in 1803 that it had been recorded in the vicinity of Tenbury (SO5968). This is probably the same record that is listed for Worcestershire in Turner & Dillwyn (1805), where it is credited to Arthur Aikin. Some authors have rejected it, but it does seem possible, and Babington's apparent endorsement does help; but it seems most likely that it would have been in the flood plain of the Teme on the Worcestershire side of the county boundary.

In 1835 Andrew Bloxam recorded it in the Mere at Ellesmere (SJ4034), and in Leighton's Flora of 1841 there are also records for Astley (SJ5218) by Edward Elsmere, Walford Pool (SJ4320) by Thomas Eyton, and at Hencott Pool again by Leighton himself.

In about 1870 the generally unreliable botanist Griffith Griffiths listed Bomere Pool (SJ4908) as a site for this species. His record was later queried by Richard Benson, but Edward Rutter rediscovered it there in 1957, so Griffiths probably deserves the benefit of the doubt in this case. It was still there in 2003 (Whild & Lockton) – the only mere in which it survives.

Frederic Stratton, a solicitor from the Isle of Wight, collected specimens at Blake Mere in 1871, so by this time it was presumably something of a celebrity for the county. Even Druce came to Ellesmere to see it in 1888.

By this time, however, the meres were in decline, and the records of *L. natans* in them become fewer. Eutrophication and increasingly frequent and severe algal blooms were probably the main cause of its demise. As for the rivers, they were also declining in quality, and after it was found in the River Perry at Boreatton (SJ3923) by Miss Ormond in 1924 it has never been recorded in a river in Shropshire again.

In 1862, however, the Reverend C.E. Parker of Torquay collected *Luronium* in the Shropshire Union Canal at Llangollen in Denbighshire. This is the earliest known record for a canal, and before long it was being found in canals in Shropshire and elsewhere. A certain W. Jones found it in the Ellesmere Canal at Rednal (SJ3527) in 1880, and in the same year W.E. Beckwith found it to be abundant in the Llangollen Canal at Cole Mere (SJ4333) and the Shrewsbury Canal at Upton Magna (SJ5511).

Although the Montgomery and Llangollen canals join at Frankton, the Shrewsbury Canal is entirely isolated, so it seems likely that the *Luronium* must have been around in the canal system for some time. How it first got there is a matter for speculation. A theory sometimes attributed to Ted Lousley is that it floated down the Dee from Llyn Tegid (Lake

Bala) to the Llangollen Canal. This theory was espoused by O.M. Feilden as early as 1906, but neither Feilden nor Lousley knew that *Luronium* was also present in Llyn Ebyr, in the headwaters above the other end of the Montgomery Canal, where it was not discovered until 1988. Alternatively, it could as easily have entered the canal system from the meres – for example, from the Mere at Ellesmere, which used to overflow into the Ellesmere (Llangollen) Canal when it was first constructed. Eventually the level of the mere was lowered to prevent that happening.

So the origin of the *Luronium* plants in the canal network is unknown. Chronologically, it was the Mere at Ellesmere that was first connected to the canals in about 1800, but as it was 62 years later that *Luronium* was first recorded, that does not answer the question. Isozyme studies by Kay and John at the University of Swansea (Kay, John & Jones, 1999) are inconclusive. Their dendrogram shows variation within the population in the Montgomery Canal, but they did not sample the meres, nor any length of canal in England, so it is impossible to draw any firm conclusions. However, a genetic approach might well succeed if sufficient numbers of samples are analysed. It is a question that matters, because the lowland populations of *Luronium* are nearly extinct now, and if they are genetically distinct from the upland ones, the canals could be providing a valuable refugium.

Other records for canals include the Llangollen Canal at Whixall Moss (Augustin Ley, 1882) and at Ellesmere (J.D. Gray, 1893 & 1898), and the Prees Branch Canal (SJ4934), where it was found by Charles Sinker in 1966. After the canals fell into disuse between the wars, they began to dry up, and inevitably the *Luronium* disappeared. Trina Paskell found it still present at Keeper's Bridge (Jones's Rednal site) in 1978, but by 1988 Chris Walker reported it gone from there. Restoration of canals for motorised boat traffic has been a disaster for conservation, even with the construction of off-line reserves and pools, which have failed to sustain populations of *Luronium*. The last record of it in a canal in Shropshire was in 1994, when British Waterways staff 'rescued'

it from Aston Locks prior to reconstruction. Given clear water, there is every chance it could return, and it is still abundant in the Welsh sections of the Montgomery Canal, but even low levels of boat traffic seem to have an immediate and devastating effect.

In 1955 Edward Rutter discovered a new site for it at Brown Moss (SJ5639). Although this is sometimes considered one of the meres, it is not typical because it is a series of shallow pools with fluctuating water levels. The site is common land, and like many other commons it became overgrown when grazing rights were no longer exercised in the latter half of the 20th century. The last confirmed record of *Luronium* there was in 1986, when Mary Fuller photographed it. Since then there have been several records, but they appear to be errors for *Alisma plantago-aquatica*.

In 2003 Kate Thorne discovered an entirely new site for it in the floodplain of the Severn at Melverley (SJ3418), growing in a seasonally flooded hollow in a field of cow pasture. Presumably it was brought here by the river in spate, but how long it had been growing there is unknown. The population was large and vigorous, with hundreds of robust plants.

Luronium natans

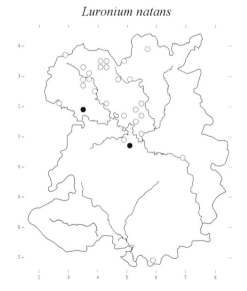

It seems from these records that *Luronium natans* has several distinct ecological niches. It grows in deep lakes with low nutrient levels that restrict the growth of other plants.

It also used to occur in rivers, where presumably the current and the shifting substrate created sufficient open areas to allow the *Luronium* to thrive. There may be some association with mires, as the rivers involved drain peat bogs such as Wem Moss, Whixall Moss and Baggy Moor.

A third habitat is in shallow ponds, often on heathy soils such as at Ebreywood, Shawbury Heath, Astley, Wem, Walford Pool, Brown Moss and Melverley. In this habitat, it is probably a combination of grazing and fluctuating water levels that maintain the open conditions necessary for the *Luronium*.

Finally, there are the canals, which are kept open only by constant management. A period of ten or twenty years of neglect is sufficient to allow the marginal plants – especially *Glyceria maxima* – to close over the water altogether and shade out the *Luronium*. Boating the canals with motorised craft generates so much suspended silt that the *Luronium* is soon eliminated by a lack of light.

Lycopodiella inundata L.
Marsh Clubmoss
Native. Extinct (1849).

The only record of this species in Shropshire dates from between 1846 and 1849, when Holland Sandford collected it at Brown Moss (SJ5639). It was identified by J.C. Melvill in 1912, but the current location of the specimen is unknown. It is a plant of bare peat, and is still quite widespread in Britain in areas of suitable habitat, but it has disappeared from the Midlands.

Lycopodium clavatum L.
Stag's-horn Clubmoss
Native. Scarce.

The first record of this species in the county comes from Cox's Natural History of Shropshire (1720-1731), where it was recorded by 'a Student of Physick' on the Stiperstones (ca. SO3698). The student in question may have been Littleton Brown.

Edward Williams also found it there in about 1800. The Stiperstones range is still the best

site for it, although the plants do not always occur in the same place. Leighton recorded it at Castle Ring (SJ3701) in about 1841, whereas Sinker had it at Perkins Beach (SO3699) in 1968. In more recent times it has been recorded along the top of the former Gatten Plantation (SO3698), where it was first found by Joyce Warren in 1979 and has since been seen many times, most recently in 2002 (Whild & Lockton). David Hatfield found a new site at Nipstone Rock (SO3597) in 2002.

Lycopodium clavatum

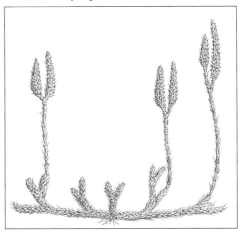

Williams also found it at Hodnet Heath (SJ6226) and Bettws-y-crwyn (SO2081) in about 1800. Joseph Babington recorded it on Bedstone Hill (SO3575) in 1803. Leighton added Caer Caradoc (SO4795) and Brown Clee (SO5986) to the site list in 1841.

In Diamond's Flora of Oswestry (1891) it is reported to occur on heaths in the district, although the district in question extended into Wales, so this might not be a record for Shropshire. Richard Benson found it at Underhill Hall (SJ4000) in 1893. A specimen collected by William Brookes at Beaumont Hill, Quatford (presumably Bowmanshill, SO7391, some time before 1895) is at Shrewsbury Museum. T.P. Blunt recorded it at Bury Ditches (SO3284) in 1895, and H.E. Forrest had it at Woolstaston (SO4598) the same year.

W.B. Allen recorded it at Benthall (SJ6602) in 1902, and William Phillips made a record for the 'Church Stretton Hills' – presumably

Caer Caradoc, as he generally copied Leighton – in 1904.

In Hamilton's missing Flora of 1913 there were apparently records for SO39E, which was presumably Stapeley Hill, and SO67Y (Wyre Common?). J.B. Duncan found it on Black Hill (SO3279) in 1913. In 1965 H.H. Shepherd recorded it at Tueshill Wood (= Bucknell Wood, SO3374) and at about the same time G.P. Richards recorded it at Kinsley Wood (SO2872).

Lycopodium clavatum

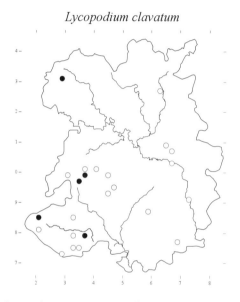

It continues to crop up in new sites, but it rarely persists for long. David Harding recorded it on the Ercall (SJ6409) in the 1970s, but it has not been seen there since. Marjorie Wainwright discovered it on Old Oswestry (SJ2931) in 1981, where it has also been seen by John Thompson (1992-1995), Rachel Thomas (1996) and Sarah Whild (1999), but it seems to have gone from there now. Ian Trueman found it in an opencast clay pit at Stoneyhill (SJ6606) in 1984, and it persisted there until 1991 (J.D. Box). John Clayfield found it at Purslow Wood (SO3678) in 2001 and there a small patch at Rhos Fiddle (SO2085, Lockton & Whild) in 2002.

There are therefore just four currently known sites for it in the county, although it is almost certainly present elsewhere, as it is such a difficult plant to find. In Britain it is largely restricted to (but frequent in) the north and west.

Marrubium vulgare L.
White Horehound
Archaeophyte. Rare.

It is generally considered that White Horehound is an introduction in most of Britain. It was formerly widespread along roadsides and on disturbed soils over limestone or chalk. In Shropshire it was once reasonably common. Williams recorded it at Bridgnorth (SO7192) and Cross Houses (SJ5307) in about 1800. Leighton (1841) gives records for Benthall Edge (SJ6503), Ensdon (SJ4016), Hopton Cliff (SJ3820), Llanymynech Hill (SJ2622, Dovaston), Ludlow (SO5175, McGhie), Oreton (SO6580, Jorden), Shawbury Heath (SJ5420), The Morfe (SO7692, Crotch) and Wenlock Edge (SO5997, Brookes).

Beckwith considered it a garden escape on Charlton Hill (SJ5807) in 1880, but he then found it on a hedge-bank near Eyton on Severn (SJ5706) in 1882. Diamond (1891) lists Selattyn (SJ2633) and Llanymynech (SJ2620). In 1901 A.R. Horwood found it at Marrington (SO2796); in 1903 W.B. Allen saw it at Cound Lodge (SJ5505); and in 1904 Potts & Allen recorded it at Ironbridge (SJ6703).

It was recorded at Prees Higher Heath (SJ5636) by J. Ramsbottom in 1907 and at Redhill (SJ4609) and Pontesbury (SJ3805) by J.B. Johnson in 1908 and 1910 respectively.

Norah Mackenzie seems to have been the first to record it at Boreton Bank (SJ5106) in 1950, where it has subsequently been seen by Rutter (1955), Sinker (1965), Thorne (1990), and by Stokes (1994 & 1997). This is probably the only current site for it in the county.

Other recent records in Sinker's Flora may all be of garden escapes: Henry Hand recorded it at Pedlar's Rest (SO4884) in the 1970s; and Dan Daniels had it at Stoney Stretton (SJ3809), Edge (SJ3908) and Aston Rogers (SJ3406), all in 1977.

Melica nutans L.
Mountain Melick
Native. Rare.

This species occurs in woodland and on limestone exposures in the north and west of Britain, and is on the edge of its range in Shropshire. It was collected in the Wyre Forest by Edwin Lees and Andrew Bloxam in about 1841, and it has subsequently been seen there many times, most notably by John Bingham, who found it in the following monads in the 1970s: SO7476, SO7576, SO7676 & SO7577. In 1986 he added the square SO7376 to the list.

In 1996 Jackie Pedlow found it at Blodwel Rocks (SJ2623, conf. M. Wainwright) – the first record for this part of the county, although it is known in adjacent parts of Montgomeryshire.

Mentha pulegium L.
Pennyroyal
Archaeophyte. Extinct (2002).

Pennyroyal occurs in a similar habitat to that of *Chamaemelum nobile*, along winter-wet, summer-dry roadsides. Edward Williams recorded it on Rodington Heath (SJ5814) and Evenwood Common (SJ5501), presumably in its typical habitat of common land by roads. An anonymous record in Turner & Dillwyn's Botanist's Guide (1805) was for Caynham Camp (SO5473); John Evans also recorded it in 1805 in wet fields at Llanymynech (SJ2621); and George Jorden listed it for the Wyre Forest (in Shropshire, Worcestershire or possibly Staffordshire) in 1856. Two records given in Sinker's Flora of 1985, for Gorstley (SO5874, C. Raikes, 1977) and Steadvallets (SO4676, T. Mitchell, 1979) seem dubious and are best ignored.

It was therefore nearly 200 years since the last record when it was found by Sarah Whild along a disused railway in Shrewsbury (SJ5110) in 2002. It could have been a garden escape, but it could equally have come from buried seed in the verge of the old Roman road, a few metres away. It was later transplanted by County Council staff to make way for a new cycle path, but it did not survive.

Minuartia hybrida (Vill.) Schischk.
Fine-leaved Sandwort
Archaeophyte. Extinct (1878).

This species occurs on light, often disturbed soils such as in arable fields, in the south-east of Britain. Shropshire is rather beyond the edge of its range. It was recorded by Francis Dickinson in fields near Sharpstones Hill (SJ4909) in 1841 and again by William Phillips in 1878. It seems most appropriate to consider it a former agricultural weed in this county, and therefore an archaeophyte.

Monotropa hypopitys L.
Yellow Bird's-nest
Native. Rare.

In about 1796 Arthur Aikin found two plants of Yellow Bird's-nest in the woods between Coalbrookdale and Coalport (SJ6803).

It was not until September 1892 that it was recorded again. G. St. George Poole found it in 'a wood near Craven Arms' and J. Bowen recorded it in 'a wood near Ludlow' at the same time. These are surely the same place. Druce, in 1911, described the site as 'near Stokesay,' which is probably Stoke Wood (SO4281).

George Potts found it in Tick Wood (SJ6403) in 1912, and W.B. Allen recorded it there in 1922. Potts then found it at Benthall Edge (SJ6603) in 1927, where Paul Benthall saw it in 1980, T.A. Gilmour recorded it in 1983, and John Box saw it in 1984 and 1985.

Charles Sinker discovered it at Blodwel Rocks (SJ2623) in 1962 but it has not been seen there since. In 1974 Kathleen Saville found it in ash woodland at Lilleshall Quarry on Wenlock Edge (SJ5796), where there were initially 66 plants, but this had risen to over 100 by 1975 (Audrey Franks). It was last recorded there by Saville in 1976, and in 1993 it was present at Blakeway Coppice (SO5897, W.V. Prestwood & M. Davies).

Most of these sites seem to be W8 *Fraxinus excelsior - Acer campestre - Mercurialis perennis* woodland in limestone areas. It may well be under-recorded.

Monotropa hypopitys

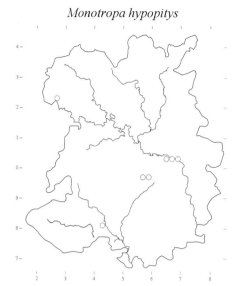

Myosurus minimus L.
Mousetail
Neophyte. Extinct (1970).

The only record of this plant in Shropshire was by Philip Oswald, who found it on the edge of an arable field near Betton Pool (SJ5108) in 1970.

Myosurus minimus

Myrica gale L.
Bog Myrtle
Native. Rare.

In Shropshire this species seems to be restricted to drying peat bogs. The first record was by R.H. Waring, at the Decoy near

Babbinswood (SJ3229) in 1770. Edward Williams saw it at Lee (SJ4032) in about 1800, when this area was being drained for the construction of the Montgomery Canal. Thomas Eyton recorded it on a moss near Walford (SJ4320) and at The Yesters (SJ4321) in 1841.

Andrew Bloxam found it still at Ellesmere in 1841, where it was later seen by Beckwith in 1880 and by Diamond and Beacall in 1891. Leighton found it in great abundance at Twyford Vownog (SJ3426) – part of the Rednall Moss complex – in 1841.

Beckwith (1880) found it at Crose Mere (SJ4230) – possibly the same site as Sinker's 1958 record for Whattal Moss - and at Blake Mere (SJ4133), where it has since been recorded by Wigginton (1979) and Walker (1991).

Wem Moss (SJ4734) is the only site where it is currently found. It seems to have been recorded there first by Edward Wilson in 1950, and subsequently by Rose & Bellamy (1959), Sinker (1962), Keith Bell (1977), Walker (1986), and others. In 2004 it was abundant and continuing to spread across much of the surface of the drying mire (Lockton).

A seemingly anomalous site is Millmoors (SJ8092), where Bryan Fowler recorded a single bush by a stream in 1980 and 1986.

Myrica gale

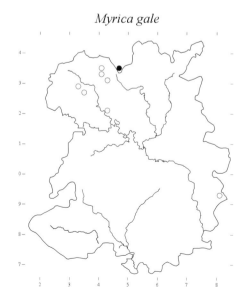

Myriophyllum alterniflorum DC.
Alternate Water-milfoil
Native. Scarce.

Andrew Bloxam holds the first British record of this species, which he found in a pond by the side of the canal near Whixall Moss (SJ4935) and near Cole Mere (SJ4333) in 1836. It is a plant of clear, oligotrophic waters, and was once quite widespread in the English lowlands but is now very rare. It is still frequent in upland areas, however.

Leighton (1841) recorded it at Berrington Pool (SJ5207), Cole Mere (SJ4333), Morda Pool (SJ2828), Rednal Moss (SJ3426) and The Mere, Ellesmere (SJ4034). Phillips reported that it was still at Berrington Pool in 1878, and in 1896 W.P. Hamilton found it at Betton Pool. Since then it has not been recorded in any of the meres & mosses.

In 1977 Joan Connell found it in the River Perry at Fitz (SJ4418, det. P.A. Wolseley), but the only other river it has been recorded in is the Tanat at Llanyblodwel (SJ2322), where it just makes it into the county after being quite frequent in Wales (Lockton, 1994).

Myriophyllum alterniflorum

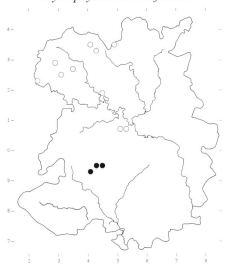

It was first discovered on the Long Mynd by Audrey Ashwell in 1982, in a pond on the golf course (SO4494), and has since been seen there by Joyce Warren (1986 & 1991) and Kate Thorne (2000). It was abundant in the reservoir and in several pools along the stream in New Pool Hollow (SO4394) in 1999 (Whild & Lockton, conf. C.D. Preston) and in four of the pools at Pole Cottage (SO4193, Thorne).

Rashmi Dave recorded it in the Montgomery Canal at Maesbury Marsh (SJ3124) in 1986.

Myriophyllum verticillatum L.
Whorled Water-milfoil
Native. Extinct (1897).

This is a plant of base-rich waters, not common, but widespread, in Britain. It occurs in shallow, slow-moving water in ditches and canals. Edward Williams recorded it at Eaton upon the Weald Moors (SJ6514) in about 1800, where it was later recorded by Beckwith in 1880. Henry Bidwell found it at nearby Sidney Moor (SJ6416) in 1841 (conf. Leighton) and R. Anslow listed it as a plant of the Weald Moors in 1865. By 1897 it had spread to the Newport Canal at Kynnersley (SJ6816, Phillips), but it has not been recorded in this region since then.

There are several other sites in the county where it has been recorded just once. Williams recorded it in a pond at Golding (SJ5403) and at Blake Mere (SJ4133) in about 1800; in Leighton's Flora of 1841 there is a record by Mary McGhie for a canal near Ludlow (presumably the Leominster Canal at Woofferton, SO5168); and in 1897 William Painter collected it at Hem Mill (SJ7205, conf. G.C. Druce).

Two recent records seem somewhat dubious. In 1979 Joan Connell apparently collected it in the River Severn at Isle Grange (SJ4516, det. P.A. Wolseley) and Sarah Stafford recorded it further upstream at Loton Park (SJ3417). It has not been found in the Severn again, and the habitat does not seem right. The explanation may be that the key to *Myriophyllum* given in British Water Plants (Haslam, Sinker & Wolseley 1975, p. 259) puts too much emphasis on the number of leaves in a whorl and could lead to erroneous determinations. Unless further evidence turns up, it is probably best to disregard the records from the Severn.

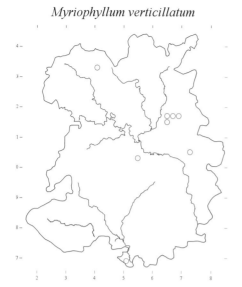

Myriophyllum verticillatum

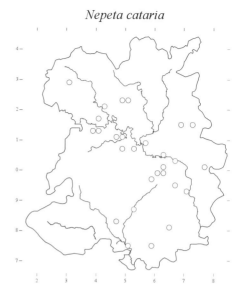

Nepeta cataria

Nepeta cataria L.

Cat-mint

Archaeophyte. Extinct (1993).

This species was once quite common in lowland England, occurring on roadsides and in hedgebanks, especially on calcareous soils. The current view is that it was introduced as a garden herb, and the naturalised populations have been in decline for many years.

Edward Williams recorded it in seven localities – mostly on roadsides – in about 1800, and Leighton added thirteen more in his Flora of 1841. These included the ruins of Lilleshall Abbey (SJ7314, R.G. Higgins) and Wenlock Abbey (SJ6200, W.P. Brookes). Beckwith listed three sites for it in 1882; Diamond (1891) lists one in the Oswestry area; and other recorders such as Phillips, Benson, Potts and Druce made individual records in the late 19th and early 20th centuries. J.C. Melvill made an interesting discovery in 1905, when it turned up in the Roman ruins at Viroconium (SJ5608), and the following year it was abundant. It was still there when Rutter recorded it in 1954, but the last record was by Sinker in 1962.

The only recent records of it are from a roadside hedge near Culmington (SO4682, H. Hand, 1977); on waste land at Colleybrook Green (SO5894, R. Rowe, 1982); and along Blakeway Hollow on Wenlock Edge (SO6099, Whild, 1993).

Nuphar pumila (Timm.) DC

Least water-lily

Native. Rare.

In 1854 Thomas Cox of Ellesmere published a letter in *The Phytologist* in which he claimed to have found *N. pumila* in 'a mere near here.' Precisely which mere he meant remains a mystery, and some authors have speculated that it occurred in most of them. However, it has only been formally recorded in three. At Blake Mere (SJ4133) it was first recorded by Diamond in 1891 and was subsequently seen by J.W. Heath in 1894, Sinker in 1970 and lastly by E.A. Wilson in 1973. At Cole Mere (SJ4333) it was again first recorded by Diamond in 1891, and subsequently by Heath in 1894, E.R. Lloyd (1927), E.A. Wilson (1954 & 1973), S.R. Turner (1967), Sinker (1970), Wigginton (1979), Walker (1985 & 1990), and Whild (1995-2003). The third site is Kettle Mere (SJ4134), where Beckwith recorded it in 1882.

Two records stand out as rather curious. J.W. Heath also seems to have listed Yetchley's (SJ4534) as a site for it in 1894. That is a part of Lyneal Moss, and it is an unlikely plant to find on a moss with no standing water; but it is possible that this might have been a reference to the Llangollen Canal, which runs alongside Lyneal Moss and close to the other meres where it is found. In 1958 Francis Rose apparently recorded it at Crose Mere (SJ4230), but that may have been the result of confusion with Cole Mere, and seems to have led to an incorrect listing in *A Nature Conservation Review* (Ratcliffe 1977).

There never have been any other sites for this species in England & Wales, but it is recorded in 48 squares in Scotland in the New Atlas. It still persists at Cole Mere, where just one small population remained at the west end of the lake in 2003 (Whild). The main threat to its survival seems to be shade from overhanging trees, but eutrophication and physical damage by boats may also be contributing to the decline. In Shropshire it is believed to be a glacial relic that somehow survived in these three meres while it died out everywhere else. The hybrid *Nuphar* ^x*spenneriana* (*N. lutea* × *pumila*) has recently been recorded at Hatch Mere in Cheshire (Whild, 2001) and at Betton Pool (SJ5107, Lockton, 2003). Whether it is native or introduced at these sites is unknown.

Oenanthe lachenalii C. Gmel.
Parsley Water-dropwort
Neophyte. Extinct (1980).

It seems unlikely that this coastal species was ever anything other than a casual in Shropshire. R. Anslow allegedly recorded it on the Weald Moors (ca. SJ6717) in about 1865; William Phillips collected it at Sharpstones Hill (SJ4909, det. W.P. Hamilton) in 1872; and Pat Wolseley found a plant on the towpath of the Montgomery Canal at Queen's Head (SJ3326) in 1980.

Ononis spinosa L.
Spiny Restharrow
Native. Rare.

There are not many good records of this species in Shropshire. A spiny form of Common Restharrow, *Ononis repens*, is apparently often confused with it (cf. New Atlas), and it is noticeable that there are very few records for the county by first rate botanists, and no voucher specimens are known.

Leighton (1841) did not record it at all, although he did give two records for *O.*

arvensis var. *spinosa* (= *O. repens*) by Edward Williams. William Phillips repeated one of these in 1878, so it was presumably still *O. repens*.

William Beckwith was the main perpetrator of records of *O. spinosa*, which he found to be more widespread than *O. repens*. He recorded it at Coalport (SJ6902), Dryton (SJ5806), Ironbridge (SJ6703), Sheinton (SJ6103), Hadnall (SJ5220), Harley (SJ5901), Leighton (SJ6105) and under Wenlock Edge (SJ5901) between 1880 and 1889. Phillips also claimed to have seen it at Coalport in 1892, as did Hildred Bigwood in 1953. The latter had an extensive herbarium, so perhaps a specimen will turn up one day.

George Potts recorded it near Linley Station (SO6898) in 1901 and on Wenlock Edge (SJ5998) in 1903. William Hunt Painter's record for Benthall (SJ6602) in 1901 seems irrefutable - he even recorded the spiny form of *O. repens* on Wenlock Edge a few years later. Gilbert Johnson recorded it at Hadnall (SJ5220) in 1912, but he was only 23 at the time and should not be considered infallible.

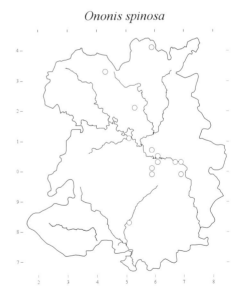

Ononis spinosa

Keith Bell recorded it near Cole Mere (SJ4233) in 1976, but Sinker did not accept that record for his Flora. Mary Fuller found it on a roadside at Lydehole (SO5182) in 1978, and photographed it there in 1982. Her plant certainly seems to have the right shaped leaves for *O. spinosa* but without a specimen it is difficult to be sure.

In 1984 V.A. Banbury collected it in fields at Robertsford (SJ5111), and the specimen was apparently confirmed by Helen Matthews. Helen Vickers reported that it was still there in 1987.

Ophrys insectifera L.
Fly Orchid
Native. Extinct (1944).

William Penny Brookes recorded this plant in a field at Rowley (S5999) and on limestone rocks at Farley (SJ6302) in Leighton's Flora of 1841. These probably represent its two native habitats in Britain – in calcareous flushes and on limestone or chalk exposures.

George Potts found it at The Vineyards (SJ6502) in 1902 and at Shirlett (SO6597) in 1921 & 1926. In 1924 a certain Mrs Ellis reported that it used to occur at Spoonhill (SO6195). It was subsequently recorded at The Vineyards by Potts in 1930, 1932 and 1941; by M. Gepp & L.C. Lloyd in 1940; and finally by D. Mason in 1943 & 1944.

Orchis ustulata L.
Burnt Orchid
Native. Extinct (1904).

This is a species of closely-grazed calcareous grasslands. It was first recorded in Shropshire by Thomas Purton in 1817 at Woodlands, Bridgnorth (SO7188). Leighton (1841) reports that Salwey found it at The Lodge near Ludlow (Overton Lodge, SO5072) and Corbett recorded it in a field near Sallow Coppice, Upper Millichope (SO5089). In 1882 Beckwith described it as 'rather frequent in some grass-fields under Wenlock Edge, near Harley' (SJ5901). W.E. Thompson searched unsuccessfully for it at Upper Millichope, but found it at Munslow (SO5287) in 1900; and W. Beacall did apparently refind it in the Millichope locality in about 1904. It has not been recorded in Shropshire since then. A record for Downton Gorge in 1803 should be attributed to Herefordshire.

Orobanche minor Sm.
Common Broomrape
Native. Rare.

Edwin Lees recorded *Orobanche elatior*, Knapweed Broomrape, in a field of clover at the foot of the Wrekin (SJ6208) in 1824. This was almost certainly *O. minor*, which is parasitic on clover.

In 1880 Beckwith found it in a field of Red Clover, *Trifolium pratense*, near Berrington (SJ5306). This was the first correct record of it in the county. Benson recorded it in a clover field at Stapleton (SJ4403) in 1892, and it came up in abundance after the clover had been harvested in June 1897. It was also abundant in two field of clover (following a crop of barley) opposite Stapleton Post Office in 1898.

T.F. Poole and William Phillips recorded it on Sweet Pea, *Lathyrus odoratus*, in a garden in Dorrington (SJ4702) in 1900, and apparently on parsnips (*Pastinaca sativa* ssp. *hortensis*) the following year.

Orobanche minor

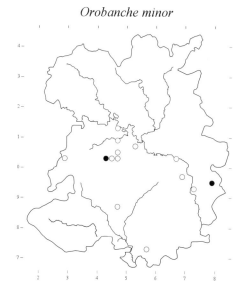

William Allen had it in a clover field at Benthall (SJ6602) in 1906, and Frances Pitt noted it occurring for several years on clover at The Albynes, Bridgnorth (SO6997). Honor Pendlebury recorded it near Marton Pool, Chirbury (SJ2902) in 1955.

Joan Connell found it growing on Hemlock, *Conium maculatum*, at Shelton (SJ4613) in 1975 (conf. Sinker). Kate Thorne recorded it on clover at Church Pulverbatch (SJ4202) in 1976, and apparently on a garden *Senecio* in 1981 and 1999. M. Badlan recorded it at Rockhill Farm, Greete (SO5772) in 1978. Winifred Hutton found it under a privet, *Ligustrum ovalifolium*, hedge in Bridgnorth (SO7292) in 1978.

In 1993 Rob Stokes found it on waste ground near the railway at Hook-a-gate (SJ4609), and in 1997 Joan Brown found it in a field of clover at Claverley (SO7894).

Orobanche rapum-genistae Thuill
Greater Broomrape
Native. Scarce.

This plant is a parasite of leguminous shrubs, especially broom and gorse, usually growing in hedge banks, rough grassland and scrub, often with a southerly aspect. It seems to be an indicator of unimproved grassland in areas that were once wooded and retain some of the ground flora. In Britain it has suffered a serious decline, especially in the eastern half of the country.

Richard Waring was the first to record it in Shropshire, at The Hayes near Oswestry SJ2830) in 1770. There are six records in Leighton's Flora of 1841: in plantations at Neach Hill (SJ7906, Lloyd); in a field opposite Quatford Church (SO7390, Bidwell); by the Montgomery Canal at Queen's Head (SJ3326, Dovaston); Sharpstones Hill (SJ4909, Leighton); Shortwood (SO5178, McGhie); and Willey Park (SO6699, Brookes).

Griffith Griffiths recorded it at Cound (SJ5505) in about 1870. Phillips was probably shown it by Leighton at Sharpstones Hill in 1878. Beckwith saw it in two places in 1880: at Brockholes Bank (SJ6106) and near Acton Burnell (SJ5302).

The soils of the Long Mynd seem particularly favourable for it, and it was first recorded there in dingles at Pulverbatch (SJ4202) by Richard Benson and at Castle Place (SJ4403) by William Beacall in 1892. It was then found at Smethcott (SO4599) by W.E.

Thompson and Beacall in 1904; at Ashes Hollow by Beacall, also in 1904; and at Mouse Hill Coppice (SO4695) by E.S. Cobbold in 1907. Helen Davidson found it at Worsley (SO4596) and Bagbatch (SO4693) in 1979, and it was still in both places in 2000 (Thorne) and 2001 (M. Cousins) respectively. Kate Thorne refound it at Pulverbatch in 1998.

Away from the Long Mynd, it was found on Hope Bowdler Hill (SO4793) by W.H. Painter in 1897; on Wenlock Edge (ca. SO5998) by Augustin Ley and William Moyle Rogers in 1907; at Hem Farm (SO6998) and The Albynes (SO6997) by Frances Pitt in 1915 and 1916 respectively. It was refound at Hem Farm by Ken Perry in 2002, but it has not been recorded at The Albynes since 1921 (Pitt).

In 1923 Mr A. & Miss K. White recorded it at Pontesbury. This is probably a reference to Earl's Hill (SJ4004), where it was also recorded by Honor Pendlebury in 1939.

Mary Fuller found it at Aston Munslow (SO5187) in 1976, but it had gone by 1986, by which time the gorse had been cleared.

In 1990 Trueman and Whild discovered a new site at Bank Farm, Habberley (SJ3804), where it still was in 1992 (Nigel Jones), and 1993 (Whild). Although this is a County Council property, the Broom was cleared and the Broomrape was lost; but then some more plants appeared on the edge of nearby Poles Coppice in 2000 (Whild & Lockton).

John Thompson seems to have been the first to notice it at Old Oswestry (SJ2931) in 1995. At first it was very rare – just three spikes in 1996 (Thompson), but this number had increased to 100 by 1997, when Frank Perring & Sarah Whild saw it there. There were 40 plants in 1998 (Muse & Trueman) and 49 in 1999 (Whild & Lockton), but then the owners – English Heritage – cleared the Broom and by 2000 it was 'rare' again (Mileto). It was not seen in that location again, but in 2002 it reappeared some distance away (Whild, Swindells & Godfrey) and increased to 20 spikes in 2003, only to decline again to 3 spikes in 2004 (Whild & Lockton).

New sites are still being found. In 2003 Peter Knights & John Mason found it at Yell Bank (SO5096), and in 2004 Tom Holland found it near Bucknell (SO3573).

Orobanche rapum-genistae

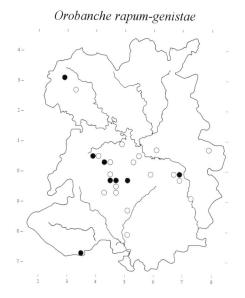

Osmunda regalis L.
Royal Fern
Native. Scarce.

Royal Fern tends to occur in Shropshire either in sandy heaths or on raised mires, especially on the edges of dystrophic pools. It was first recorded in the county by Arthur Aikin in August 1796, at Knockin Heath (SJ3521), which was an area so sandy that there were dunes, and small mires used to occur in the hollows. Edward Williams saw it in about 1800 at Birch (SJ4033), which was part of the extensive mire south of The Mere, Ellesmere; near Queen's Head – probably at Rednall Moss (SJ3427), before it was drained for the Montgomery Canal; and at Shawbury Heath (SJ5420).

Leighton collected it at West Felton (SJ3425) in 1834, and at some point collected it at Twyford Vownog (SJ3426), possibly where Williams had seen it. Robert Garner found it at Gravenhunger Moss (SJ7342) in 1844. Thomas Salwey recorded it at Maesbury (SJ3025) in 1855, a site which is also listed in Diamond (1891). This could be Morton Pool (SJ3023), where there are two or three enormous plants, 2m high and 3m across, that must be decades if not hundreds of years old. They were first recorded there by Andrew Hearle & Chris Walker in 1986, and were still thriving in 2003 (Whild & Lockton), but the site, despite being a SSSI, is degrading due to drainage and eutrophication.

Phillips (1877) gives several records. In 1862 Anslow recorded it at Rodington Heath (SJ5814); in 1870 Alfred Marston saw it on the Clee Hills (SO57/58) and at Shawbury Heath again; and Leighton saw it at Cole Mere (SJ4333) and Sandford (SJ3423). Anslow also saw it at Ellerdine Common (SO6020) and Hodnet Heath (SJ6226); W.T. Burges found it on the mire between Blake Mere and Kettle Mere (SJ4133); and a certain Miss Brown saw it at Hopton Wood (S)6276), Cleobury Mortimer (SO6775), and Stanley (SO7195). It is not certain that all of Miss Brown's records were of wild plants.

In 1882 George Davies reported that it 'used to grow in great beauty and luxuriance' at The Mere, Ellesmere (SJ4034) but went on to suggest that it may have been eradicated there by fern collectors. However, there is a specimen from there at Shrewsbury Museum, dated 1883, so it was apparently not quite gone. Diamond considered it to be still there in 1891, and it was recorded as recently as 1965.

In 1885 Mr C.B. Powell found it growing at Higher Lacon Farm, near Prees (SJ5331), and took the plant home to grow in his garden. In 1902 George Potts reintroduced it to a site at Shirlett (SO6597) from which it had been eradicated by collectors – possibly the first attempt at botanical conservation in Shropshire. But it has not been recorded there since.

Three of the most significant sites were discovered in the 1950s. Edna Lind seems to have been the first to record it at Clarepool Moss on April 6th 1950, and her description makes it apparent that this was the same plant that was still there in 2003 (Whild & Lockton). In the intervening years it had been recorded by Rose, Bellamy, Sinker, Bell, Walker & Stokes. Dr Lind, however, grossly underestimated the ecological value of Clarepool Moss and may have been partly responsible for it being overlooked as one of the first national nature reserves.

The plants at Shomere Pool were discovered by Edward Rutter in 1955, and four plants were still there in 2004 (Lockton). Rose & Bellamy found it at Wem Moss (SJ4734) in 1959, and it has fared quite well there. In 2003 surveyors from the Wildlife Trust found seven plants in the *Myrica gale*-dominated central lagg, which makes this the best site for this species in the county.

In 1971 Winifred Hutton found it in Badger Dingle (SO7699), possibly revealing the whereabouts of one of the plants raided from the wild during the fern craze. Other introduced plants have been seen at Old Rectory Wood in Church Stretton (SO4493, Helen Davidson, 1977), Hatton Grange (SJ7604, Hutton, 1981), Beckbury (SJ7601, Olive Hunter, 1982), Norton Mere (SJ7909, Hunter, 1982), Hodnet Hall (SJ6028, P. & S. Kingsbury, 1991), and Linley Hall (SO3492, Kingsbury, 1993).

Osmunda regalis

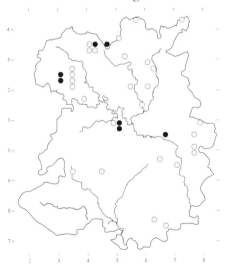

It has been found in a few other native sites recently. Martin Wigginton discovered it at Oss Mere (SJ5643) in 1979, where it still was in 1982 (J.K. Rodwell); Frank Perring saw it at Shrawardine Pool (SJ3916) in 1981, but it has gone from there now; Ian Trueman & Godfrey Blunt saw it at Whixall Moss (SJ5036) in about 1983 (it is still present on the Welsh side of the moss); and, strangely, it

turned up on a spoil heap in Telford (SJ6704) in 1996 (Whild & Lockton). In this latter site it was clearly not planted, but had most likely grown from wind-blown spores on the edge of a small acidic pool that recreated approximately its natural conditions.

Papaver dubium ssp. *lecoqii* (Lamotte) Syme
Yellow-juiced Poppy
Archaeophyte. Extinct (1908).

Although this is a fairly common agricultural weed in the south-east half of England, it has never become established in Shropshire. William Phillips was the first to record it at Welshampton (SJ4334) in 1899. W.B. Allen collected it at Benthall (SJ6602) in 1902. In 1906 J.C. Melvill found it in corn fields at Bayston Hill (SJ4808) and Pulley (SJ4709). H.M. Auden recorded it at Condover (SJ4906) in 1908. The only recent record is for a garden in Oswestry (SJ2829), where Andrew Muse found it (presumably from long buried seed) in 1998.

Parnassia palustris L.
Grass-of-Parnassus
Native. Rare.

This species is now reduced to just one site in the county. It is a plant of base-rich flushes in species-rich grassland and is indicative of some of the best wildlife habitats. The New Atlas shows that it has gone from most of lowland England.

It was first recorded at Knockin Heath (SJ3520) by Arthur Aikin in 1796. Edward Williams found it at Baschurch (SJ4221), Cound Moor (SJ5502), Golding (SJ5303), Mosterley (SJ5502) and Smythemoor (SJ6333). There are also ten sites listed in Leighton's Flora of 1841: Bitterley (SO5677, Lees), Bridgnorth (SO7094, Crotch), Cantern (SO7094, Lloyd), Crose Mere (SJ4230, Bidwell), Ellerton Hall (SJ7125, Higgins), Felton Farm (SO5076, Spare), Little Ness (SJ4019, Eyton), Maesbury (SJ3025, Salwey), Rowley (SO5999, Brookes) and Ryton (SJ4903, Corbett).

Of these sites, it was later seen at Cound Moor by Beckwith in 1880; at Maesbury by

Diamond in 1891; and at Crose Mere by many people, including Beckwith (1880), E.A. Wilson (1949), Rutter (1953), Sinker (1960), Keith Bell (1976 & 1985), Wigginton (1979), Walker (1980) and Trueman (1984). It was last recorded by Chris Walker in 1990, but seems to have been lost to succession as a result of under-management.

William Anstice recorded it near Donington Glasshouse (SJ6911) in about the 1820s. In 1849 H. Sandford found it at Brown Moss (SJ5639). In 1855 Thomas Salwey found it in meadows near Sweeny (SJ2825) and High Fawr (SJ2729). Beckwith recorded it at Church Preen (SO5498) in 1880. Diamond listed it at Treflach (SJ2525) in 1891.

George Potts recorded it at Farley Dingle (SJ6302) and nearby Bradley Coppice in 1912. G.R. Jebb found it at Wolverley (SJ4732) in 1918. Oswald Feilden had it at Welsh Frankton in 1920, but at first would not give the locality as it had become such a rare plant.

Parnassia palustris

Mary Hignett reported that it was abundant at Dolgoch Bog (SJ2724) in the late 1920s, and it lasted until the 1940s (Hignett & Asterley). J.H. Owen found it at Porth-y-waen (SJ2523) in 1946, and in 1953 Edward Wilson found about 2,000 plants somewhere near Ellesmere (SJ3934).

The first record for Trefonen Marshes (SJ2426) seems to have been by Ellen Lloyd

in about 1940, but she reported that it had died out by 1946. If so it was back by 1979, when Doris Pugh recorded it there. There are subsequent records by Walker (1986), M.A. Green (1990), M. Deadman (1991), Parker & Dawes (1992) and Walker & Wrench (1995).

Pastinaca sativa L.
Wild Parsnip
Neophyte. Rare.

Although this species is fairly common in much of England, it is absent from upland areas and western regions, and Shropshire is on the edge of its range. Leighton only gave one record of it, at Astley (SJ5218), where it was recorded by Edward Elsmere (conf. Leighton). In 1880 Beckwith found it on the Roman ruins at Wroxeter (SJ5608), where it was later seen by Melvill in 1927.

Phillips recorded it as an introduction in a quarry at Craven Arms (SO4382) in 1891; W.B. Allen found it on waste ground at Buildwas Station (SJ6404) in 1903; and Miss Auden recorded it at Condover in 1907. There are other records in Hamilton's Flora of 1913, but we do not know the details.

Ellen Lloyd found it on waste ground at Gobowen (SJ3033) in 1927; Edward Rutter recorded it at Farley Quarry (SJ6201) in 1955; G.P. Richards found it at Oreton Quarries (SO6580) in 1967; and Joan Connell reported it on the banks of the River Perry at Fitz (SJ4418). Sinker (1985) considered it extinct in the county, but it seems unlikely that it was ever anything other than a casual.

In 1987 Mary Hignett found it growing on a pavement in Oswestry (SJ2829), and in 1993 Anne Dyer recorded it being planted in a seed mix near Westhope (SO48S & SO48T) where it did not last long. In 1999 Gill Castle first recorded it at Highley-Alveley Country Park (SO7485), where it is now abundant (Wrench & Lockton, 2004). This is the true Wild Parsnip *P. sativa* ssp. *sativa,* whereas the cultivated form *P. sativa* ssp. *hortensis* has been recorded at Wolf's Head (SJ3620, Whild, 1997) and Madeley (SJ7004, Stokes, 1997).

Pastinaca sativa

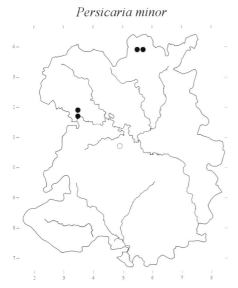

Persicaria minor (Huds.) Opiz
Small Water-pepper
Native. Rare.

Miss H.M. Auden was the first to record this species in Shropshire, at Condover (SJ4906) in 1907. It was not seen again until 1984, when Ro Fitzgerald recorded it at Brown Moss (SJ5639), where it still occurs by the side of two of the pools (pools 3b & 6) (Lockton & Whild, 2003 & 2004). In 2003 Kate Thorne found two new populations at Edgerley (SJ3417 & SJ3418), where it occurs in wet hollows in cattle-grazed pasture.

Persicaria minor

Persicaria mitis (Schrank) Assenov
Tasteless Water-pepper
Native. Extinct (1979).

There are only three records of this species in the county. William Hunt Painter recorded it at Preston upon the Weald Moors (SJ6815) in 1904; Doris Pugh found it at Cole Mere (SJ4233) in 1977; and Mary Fuller collected it at Broncroft Lodge (SO5386) in 1979 (conf. E.J. Clement). It is difficult to draw any conclusions about its ecology from such sparse information.

Phegopteris connectilis (Michx.) Watt
Beech Fern
Native. Rare.

Although this species is common in upland areas of Britain, it has declined significantly in the foothills, including in Shropshire, and is almost completely absent from the lowlands. It has been recorded in ten sites in the county, but it now survives at just two of these.

Phegopteris connectilis

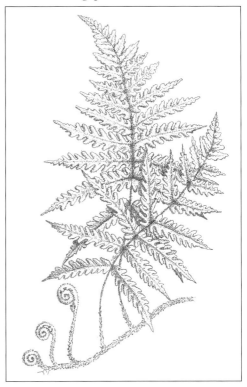

The first record was by Edward Newman, who found it in four places near the summit of Titterstone Clee (SO5977) in 1854. It has since been seen there by many people, including George Jorden (1956), Edward Rutter (1962), Charles Sinker (1965), Bill Thompson (1981), Will Prestwood (1989), Sarah Whild (1994), Clive Jermy (1998) and John Clayfield (2002). The other current site for it is Hazeldine Coppice (SO4986), where Audrey Ashwell found it in 1984 and again in 2002.

Other sites where it has been recorded include Brown Clee (SO6087, Miss Brown, 1877 & John Bingham, 1983), Craig Forda (SJ2529, Salwey, 1855), Craignant (SJ2535, Diamond, 1891), Darley Dingle (SO6899, R. Anslow, 1877), Longville Common (SO4185, A. Marston, 1870), Ragleth Wood (SO4592, G.H. Griffiths, 1870 & W. Phillips, 1877), Selattyn (SJ2633, Diamond, 1891) and Tantree Bank (SJ2806, Sinker, 1960).

Phegopteris connectilis

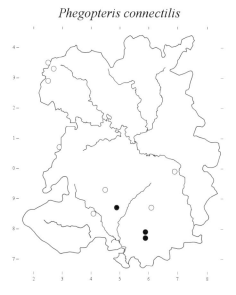

Pilularia globulifera L.
Pillwort
Native. Extinct (1962).

Pillwort is a small fern that grows in shallow water or on bare sandy soil or peat at the edges of pools and lakes. It requires clean water with low nutrient levels, and was evidently once typical of the Shropshire meres – especially those with peat bogs

associated with them. Edward Williams recorded it in about 1800 at Bomere Pool (SJ4908), Betton Alkmere (SJ5009) and in a pool between Nescliffe and Knockin (ca. SJ3721). The Reverend George Pinder found it at Gravenhunger Moss (SJ7342) in about 1844 (Garner 1844). E.F. Linton collected several specimens at White Mere (SJ4132) in 1892. In 1904 George Potts and W.B. Allen found it in the only site in the county that was not a mere: a bog at Ashfield (SO5889). Allan McGregor Stirling was the first to record it at Brown Moss (SJ5639), in 1956, and it was subsequently seen there by Gordon Graham, Charles Sinker and Edward Rutter in 1962. It is believed that, during the hot summer of 1976, the site rangers dug out pools to provide a refuge for fish, and they are said to have buried the Pillwort under the spoil, but degradation of the habitat and loss of water quality is a more convincing reason for its loss from this site.

Pimpinella major (L.) Hudson
Greater Burnet-saxifrage
Neophyte. Rare.

This is a plant of rough grassland on hedgebanks, woodland margins and road verges, mainly in limestone areas. It is common in suitable areas of England and Ireland, but almost absent from Wales and Scotland. Most of the records for Shropshire are from along roadsides. It was recorded by Edward Williams on the side of the London Road near the Redhill turnpike (SJ7310) in about 1800, and was still there when William Phillips saw it in 1904.

In 1841 Edward Elsmere found it at Hadnall (SJ5220) and Leighton recorded it at Hill Top on Wenlock Edge (SO5696); Mary McGhie reported it from Ludlow Castle Walk (SO5074). George Jorden listed it for the Wyre Forest (SO77, v.c. 38, 39 or 40) in 1856. Gilbert Johnson recorded it at Cardeston (SJ3912) in 1911. In 1925 George Potts found it still on Wenlock Edge, at Presthope (SO5897), and in 1958 Allan McGregor Stirling saw it on a roadside at Haughmond Hill (SJ5314) and near Woore (SJ7342). The only recent record was of a single plant found growing on the towpath of the Llangollen Canal (SJ4935) by Pat Parker in 1996 (conf. I.C. Trueman).

Platanthera bifolia (L.) Rich.
Lesser Butterfly-orchid
Native. Rare.

This species occurs in a range of habitats, from limestone grassland and woodland to wet heath and bogs. It has declined dramatically in the lowlands. Leighton described it as 'not unfrequent' in Shropshire in 1841, and listed twenty records. Lloyd & Rutter gave a similar account in 1957, and for Sinker's Flora project in the 1970s it was only recorded to tetrad level. Since then, however, it has almost disappeared. There is just one current site for it, at Llynclys Hill (SJ2723), where it was first recorded by Ellen Lloyd in 1929, and Jackie Pedlow counted eleven plants still there in 2003. In 1992 John Clayfield also found it on a roadside verge by Windmill Hill in Much Wenlock (SJ6200). A full list of records is given below.

Edward Williams recorded it in about 1800 at Berrington (SJ5206), Lee (SJ4032), Monkhopton (SO6293), Netchwood (SO6291) & Pitchford (SJ5303). Joseph Babington, in 1803, described it as 'very common in many places near Ludlow (SO5174) and near Bedstone (SO3675).

Leighton gave the following records in 1841: Apley Park (SO7198, Lees), Bomere Wood (SJ5007, Leighton), Buildwas (SJ6304, H. Moseley), Burwood (SO4887, Leighton), Coreley (SO6173, W. Corbett), Hawksmoor Coppice (SJ5118, Elsmere), Longnor (SJ4800, Corbett), Much Wenlock (SO6299, Brookes), Oakly Park (SO4876, Spare), Oswestry (SJ2929, Salwey), Shelve (SO3399, Bowman), Smethcott (SO4599, Corbett), Westhope (SO4887, Leighton), Whitcliffe (SO4873, J.S. Baly) and Wyre Forest (SO7576, W.G. Perry & George Jorden).

Since then it has been recorded at Oreton (SO6580, Jorden, 1856), Berrington & Bomere Wood again (Phillips, 1878), Crickheath (SJ2922), Llanymynech (SJ2620) and Selattyn (SJ2633) (Diamond, 1891), Shirlett (SO6597, Phillips, 1893), Marton Pool, Chirbury (SJ2902, Benson & Yelland,

1899), Linley (SO6898, Potts, 1902), Bettws-y-crwyn (SO2081, J.A. Panter, 1903), Eaton-under-Heywood (SO4989, W.E. Thompson, 1904), Lutwyche (SO5594) & Middlehope (SO4988) (W. Beacall, 1904), Smethcott again and Upper Millichope (SO5289, Phillips, 1904), Walkmills (SO4599, Beacall, 1904), Shirlett (SO6597, W.B. Allen & Potts, 1921), Spoad Hill (SO2580, L.F. Chitty, 1953) and Wem Moss (SJ4734, Rose & Bellamy, 1959 & Sinker, 1962).

Other squares for which Sinker gives a dot are SJ60R, SJ63Y, SO27N, SO49S, SO49Y, SO67J and SO68K.

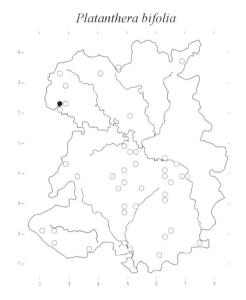

Platanthera bifolia

Polypodium cambricum L
Southern Polypody
Native. Rare.

The first record of this fern in the county was at Ludlow Castle (SO5074) in 1973 by Dick Roberts, but it has not been recorded there again. It was also reported on the wall of a pig sty at Norbury (SO3692) by Matt Busby in 1982 but has not been seen again there, either. It is a fern of calcareous substrates, and the only native place for it in the county is on cliffs at Blodwel Rocks (SJ2623), where it was first recorded by Peter Benoit in 1985 and has since been seen many times, most recently in 1998 by Ruth Dawes and Sarah Whild.

Potamogeton alpinus Balb.

Red Pondweed

Native. Rare.

It was Edward Williams who first discovered this species in Britain, at Lilleshall Mill Pool (SJ7314) in about 1804. It is largely a northern species, still frequent in Scotland and parts of Ireland, but now almost lost from the English lowlands. It grows in clear, slow-moving water but seems to have few other specific requirements. Williams also found it in a pond on Hollyhurst Common (SO4797), and in ditches at Hordley (SJ3830), Melverley (SJ3218) and Rednal (SJ3628).

In 1836, 1837, 1838 & 1841 Leighton collected it from ditches at Eyton upon the Weald Moors (SJ6514) (conf. Dandy, Taylor & Preston at BM, CGE, E, CLE & SHY), and in 1837 he also found it in a pit near Sharpstones Hill (SJ4909) (CGE, E, SHY). He also found it on 'boggy ground near the Wolf's Head turnpike' (SJ3620), and he saw a specimen collected by T.W. Wilson from near Whitchurch (SJ5441) in about 1840.

In 1847 William Newbould collected it at Bomere Pool (SJ4908, det. Dandy & Taylor, BM) and in 1878 William Phillips recorded it 'in the vicinity of Shrewsbury' (ca. SJ4912). It seems possible that this, and Wilson's Whitchurch site, were actually the canals, but the first definite records from a canal were in 1880, when Beckwith found it in the Llangollen Canal at Blake Mere (SJ4233) and Serjeantson, Beckwith & Phillips found it in the same canal at Ellesmere (SJ4034) (both conf. C.D. Preston, SHY). It was subsequently recorded in the Llangollen Canal at Ellesmere by Beckwith (1882), J.D. Gray (1893), Vera Gordon (1955) and J.K. Morton (1956); at Platt Lane (SJ5136) by Lousley in 1936; at Rhoswiel (SJ2936) by Gordon in 1956; at Welshampton (SJ4434) by Dorothy Cadbury in 1949; and at Whixall (SJ4835) by Trina Paskell in 1975.

In 1881 Phillips collected it at Blake Mere (det. Dandy & Taylor BM) but does not specify whether it was in the mere or the adjacent canal. That year Phillips collected it 'near Shrewsbury' which, by cross-reference against a record of his for *P. pectinatus*, was probably the Shrewsbury Canal at Upton Magna (SJ5511). It was never recorded in that canal again.

Serjeantson found it in a ditch near Crose Mere (SJ4230) in 1882, and in 1885 Beckwith collected it at Battlefield (SJ5116, conf. Dandy & Taylor, GL), but after that it has only been recorded in canals, except for a single rather dubious record for the River Teme at Tenbury Wells (SO5968, N.T.H. Holmes, 1980).

The first record for the Prees Branch Canal was by Sinker in 1966, and it was still there in 1975 (G. Wynne, conf. Dandy, PVT), but it must have gone from there soon after the opening of the marina.

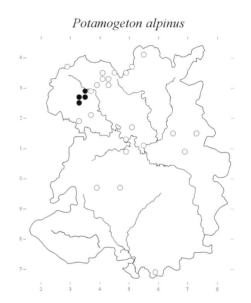

Potamogeton alpinus

The first record for the Montgomery Canal was in 1985, when John Alder recorded it near Aston Locks (SJ3326). It has since been seen there by Rashmi Dave (1986), Caroline Tandy (1987), Chris Walker (1992), Jonathan Briggs (1994), Richard Lansdown (1997), Chris Newbold (2001), and Whild & Lockton (2002). Allan Dawes reported that it was still there in 2003, but by 2004 it had gone. Although this was the most well-recorded stretch of canal, it had also been present at Heath Houses (SJ3427, Tandy, 1987), Keeper's Bridge (SJ3528, Tandy, 1987; Whild, Lockton & Lansdown, 1997-1998; & Newbold, 2001), and in the Rednal Basin

(SJ3527, Briggs, Hollier & Dave 1986; Lockton, 2002; & Newbold, 2003). Red Pondweed is not present on the Welsh lengths of the Montgomery Canal, so the loss of this species from the Shropshire parts is particularly significant. It still survives as an introduction in the Aston Locks Reserve (SJ3326, R.A. Dawes, 2004).

Potamogeton ^x*angustifolius* J. Presl

(*P. gramineus* × *lucens*)

Long-leaved Pondweed

Native. Extinct (1892).

The earliest known record for the county is a specimen in the herbarium of William Borrer, possibly collected by him at Crose Mere (SJ4230) in July 1841 (det. Dandy & Taylor, K). R.M. Serjeantson collected it in 1882 and 1885 (det. C.D. Preston, SHY); H.F. Parsons got it in 1884 (det. Preston, SLBI); and E.F. Linton was the last to find it there in 1892 (det. Dandy & Taylor, BM).

Beckwith found it at Ellesmere (SJ4034) in 1884 (det. Dandy & Taylor, CGE), and William Phillips also collected there some time in the late 19th century (det. C.D. Preston, SHY). Beckwith also found it at Frankton – presumably in the Montgomery Canal at Frankton Locks (SJ3631) in 1885 (det. Dandy & Taylor, BM).

Potamogeton coloratus Hornem.

Fen Pondweed

Native. Extinct (1882).

William Beckwith and Robert Serjeantson collected this species from ditches near Crose Mere (SJ4230) and The Mere, Ellesmere (SJ4034) in 1882 (conf. Dandy, Taylor & Preston, BM, SHY) but it has not been recorded in the county since. It grows in ditches containing base-rich water flowing over a peaty substrate, and was probably flourishing at that time as a result of drainage operations in the formerly extensive mires adjacent to those meres.

Potamogeton compressus L.

Grasswrack pondweed

Native. Extinct (2003).

There is a specimen of *P. compressus* in the herbarium of Trinity College, Dublin, from the collection of William Borrer of Henfield, Sussex. The label reads 'Shrewsbury' but it is undated and there is no other information. We do not know if Borrer ever visited Shropshire. Carter (1960) implies that he went to Stoke Wood in 1841 to see the *Astrantia major*, but it is possible that he just received a specimen from a correspondent. We do know, however, that Leighton sent him many specimens of willows, and it seems possible that the pondweed was also collected by Leighton, possibly in the Shrewsbury Canal between Shrewsbury and Uffington (SJ5305) in 1838. At that date he collected *P. friesii* and *P. obtusifolius* there and, on page 77 of his Flora, grouped them all as *P. pusillus* var. *major* (happily ignoring Borrer's determination of *P. gramineus*, which was wrong).

The second record for Shropshire is equally mysterious. A specimen was discovered in Beckwith's herbarium long after his death in 1892. It was collected in September 1884 and identified by Arthur Bennett in 1924 (later confirmed by J.E. Dandy & George Taylor). No locality is given, but we do know that Beckwith collected *P. berchtoldii* at Eaton Constantine and Cressage in the same month, and we have no other records of his during that period. The most likely explanation is that the *P. compressus* came from the Severn where it runs between those two villages (SJ5904), as there are no other obvious water bodies in the vicinity.

A few years later, in 1897, William Hamilton definitely did collect it in the Severn at Monkmoor, near Shrewsbury (SJ5114), a few miles upstream from where Beckwith might have found it. That, however, is the last time it was found in a river or any other natural water body in the county. Nearly all the records since then have been from canals. The first of these was the Llangollen Canal at Ellesmere (SJ4034), for which there is a specimen at NMW in the herbarium of Eleanor Vachell, dated May 1927. It was subsequently recorded there by Elsie Graham in 1932 and Vera Gordon in 1955. In other parts of the Llangollen Canal it was found at Whixall (SJ4835) by J.E. Lousley in 1936, by J.K. Morton in 1956, and by Goronwy Wynne in 1973. At Welshampton (SJ4434) Dorothy Cadbury collected it in 1949. The 1973 record was the last, giving us an approximate date for the decline of the water quality in the main channel of this canal.

The old Whitchurch Canal (SJ5341) and the Prees Branch Canal (SJ4934) were short side-arms branching off the Llangollen. Cadbury collected *P. compressus* in the former in 1950, and in the latter it was found by Sinker in 1966. The Prees Branch was considered one of the finest water bodies in Britain (Ratcliffe 1977), and is cited by Rodwell (1995) as a prime example of the NVC type A11 *Potamogeton pectinatus-Myriophyllum spicatum* community. Unfortunately, by the time Rodwell was writing the vegetation had long since gone. Half the canal was restored to navigation when the marina was constructed, and the other half was given to the Shropshire Wildlife Trust as a reserve. Despite assurances at the time that the aquatic plants would survive in both halves, it rapidly disappeared under the murky water of the boated sections and the dense shade of the neglected reserve. Trina Paskell listed *P. compressus* as present between 1976 and 1978, and it was cited on NCC surveys of 1984 and 1989, but the latter might have been references to earlier records rather than actual sightings.

The Montgomery Canal is now the stronghold of *Potamogeton compressus*. Due to low levels of botanical recording in Powys (there was no county Flora for Montgomeryshire until 1995) it was not until 1935 that it was first recorded there. Henry Haines, who retired from his post as Conservator of the Forests of India to Glyn Gogyan at Minafon in Powys, collected it in the Montgomery Canal at Welshpool and grew it on in a pond. A few years later, in 1838, a Miss S. Haines (his daughter?) collected and pressed a specimen from the canal itself. Whether it had been throughout the canal network since Leighton's time, and

had simply been overlooked, we do not know.

Here in Shropshire, the first record for the Montgomery Canal was in 1955, when K.M. Goodway found it in the Maesbury Marsh reach (SJ3124). It was still there in 1968 when Sinker saw it, and between 1985 and 1987 when it was recorded by John Alder, Rashmi Dave, Chris Walker and Caroline Tandy. Jonathan Briggs also recorded it as present in the Rednal Basin, a short side arm at SJ3527, where it was apparently planted. By 1995 it was gone from both these areas, and could only be found in the vicinity of Aston Locks (SJ3326), where it was seen by Pat Parker and Jane Ing, and subsequently by Richard Lansdown in 1997. This was the last place in Shropshire where it was known, and in 2002 there were just half a dozen plants left. The canal was formally reopened for navigation in the spring of 2003 and it seems not to have come up that year.

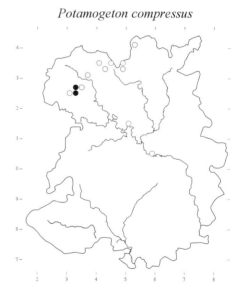

Potamogeton compressus

Grasswrack Pondweed is highly susceptible to pollution, as it requires very clear water. It has virtually disappeared from its native habitat in rivers in Britain, surviving in just a few isolated oxbow lakes. The canal populations have been devastated by the modern use of motorised boats, which stir up sediment and make the water too murky for it to survive. There are some isolated side arms and semi-derelict canals where it still occurs, but the number of suitable places is rapidly decreasing. Small populations also remain in the Norfolk Broads and in a lake in Scotland. British Waterways and English Nature have experimented with reintroductions in the Broads and throughout the canal network, but so far without success. This is therefore one of Britain's most endangered plants, but for now it still thrives in the Montgomery canal in Wales, although it appears to be extinct in Shropshire.

Potamogeton ˣcooperi (Fryer) Fryer

(*P. perfoliatus* × *crispus*)

Cooper's Pondweed

Native. Extinct (1882).

This rare hybrid was collected by William Scott from the Shrewsbury Canal at Upton Magna (SJ5511) in 1878 (det. Dandy & Taylor, BM) and by William Beckwith at Berrington Pool (SJ5207, conf. C.D. Preston, SHY) in 1880 and The Mere, Ellesmere (SJ4034, conf. Dandy & Taylor, BM) in 1882.

Potamogeton friesii Rupr.

Flat-stalked Pondweed

Native. Extinct (2003).

Henry Bidwell and William Leighton both collected this species in Shropshire in 1838. Bidwell's specimen was from Snowdon Pool (SJ7801) while Leighton's was from a more typical habitat, the Shrewsbury Canal between Shrewsbury and Uffington (ca. SJ5214). It has never been reliably recorded again from any site other than a canal in this county. The next record was not until June 1881, when it was collected by William Phillips in the Shrewsbury Canal near Upton Magna (SJ5511), and the following month Robert Serjeantson and William Beckwith also collected it there and at nearby Berwick Wharf (SJ5410). In 1884 Beckwith found it in the Llangollen Canal at Ellesmere (SJ4034), which is on an entirely separate canal system to the Shrewsbury Canal, which even carried a different size of boat, so the origin of the plants in these two sites seems unlikely to be the same.

After Beckwith there is another long gap in recording, until Dorothy Cadbury found it in the Llangollen Canal at Welshampton (SJ4434) and the Shrewsbury Canal at Long Waste (SJ6115) in 1949 and 1952 respectively. These are very close to the two historic localities. She also found it in the Whitchurch Canal (SJ5341) in 1950, which is a good distance from where it had been seen before. Given this very low level of recording, it is likely that *P. friesii* was quite widely dispersed throughout most, if not all, of the county's canals at this time.

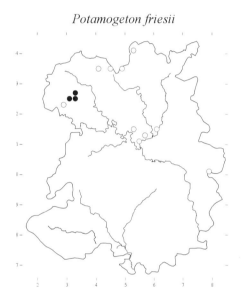

Potamogeton friesii

As if to confirm this point, students from Cambridge University collected specimens from the Montgomery Canal at Maesbury Marsh (SJ3024) in 1955, and Charles Sinker added the Prees Branch Canal (SJ4934) to the list in 1966. From the 1950s and 1960s there are also several repeat records for known sites. After that, however, the decline clearly started. Trina Paskell listed *P. friesii* as one of the species she saw in the Prees Branch Canal in the 1970s, but following restoration in the 1980s it has disappeared. It has never been recorded on any of the other canals again, either, with the sole exception of the Montgomery Canal, over a short distance around Maesbury Marsh (SJ3124 & SJ3125). Here it was seen by John Alder, Rashmi Dave, Chris Walker and Caroline Tandy between 1985 and 1987, and again by

Richard Lansdown in 1998. We (Whild & Lockton) found it to be abundant for a short distance upstream and downstream of Maesbury Marsh in 2000, but that stretch was drained in 2002 to prepare for the restoration, and *Potamogeton friesii* has not been recorded in Shropshire since.

Potamogeton gramineus L.
Various-leaved Pondweed
Native. Extinct (1885).

There are only five or maybe six sites in Shropshire where this species has been recorded, and Edward Williams found three of them in about 1800: Blake Mere (SJ4133), White Mere (SJ4132) and Berrington Pool (SJ5207). At Blake Mere and White Mere it has since only been seen by Beckwith in 1885 (det. Dandy & Taylor, BM), but until 1881 many people recorded it at Berrington Pool, including Westcombe (1826 & 1848), Leighton (1833, 1835 & 1836), Babington (1834), Serjeantson (1877), Phillips (1878), Beckwith (1880), and finally Phillips, J. Groves and Beckwith, all in 1881.

It was recorded at Cole Mere (SJ4333) by Andrew Bloxam in about 1841, and at Oss Mere (SJ5643) by Phillips & Beckwith in 1883. The only other site in the county where it has been recorded is the Weald Moors, where R. Anslow stated it occurred in 1865, although there is no specimen to confirm this.

Potamogeton ^x*griffithii* A. Benn.
(*P. alpinus* × *praelongus*)
Not in Shropshire.

Charles Sinker recorded this hybrid on the Prees Branch Canal (SJ4934) in 1966, but it is not widely accepted because there is no voucher specimen. It is best considered unconfirmed.

Potamogeton lucens L.
Shining Pondweed
Native. Extinct (1979).

There is scant evidence for this species in Shropshire. Edward Williams recorded it in 'ponds' in about 1800, but it is possible that he was looking at a different species. Henry

Spare recorded it at Oakly Park (SO4876) in 1841, but several of his records are dubious. Griffith Griffiths claimed to have seen it at Bomere Pool (SJ4908) in about 1870, but again he cannot really be trusted when identifying difficult plants. The most likely site for it was at Marton Pool, Chirbury (SJ2902), where Richard Benson and W. Yelland recorded it in 1899, and where Martin Wigginton found a fragment of a leaf in 1979. The only confirmed record is a specimen from Wellington (SJ6511) which was collected by F.R. Tennant in 1955 (conf. Dandy & Taylor, CGE), presumably in a canal or a reservoir associated with the canal system.

Potamogeton praelongus Wulfen
Long-stalked Pondweed
Native. Extinct (1995).

This is described by Preston (1995) as a plant of deep, clear water. It is now very rare in the English lowlands, but is still fairly frequent in Scotland and Ireland. In Shropshire it has been recorded in several meres and canals.

Phillips & Beckwith found it floating in the Llangollen Canal at Ellesmere (SJ4034) in 1880, but surmised that it must have come from White Mere (SJ4132), as it didn't seem to be growing in the canal. In 1881 Serjeantson & Beckwith found it in the Shrewsbury Canal at Berwick Wharf (SJ5411). Beckwith found it to be abundant in deep places in White Mere in 1882 (conf. Dandy & Taylor, BM), and in 1883 someone (probably Beckwith) found it at Oss Mere (conf. Dandy & Taylor, BM).

William Beacall recorded it in the Llangollen Canal at Cole Mere (SJ4333) in 1891, and it was later collected in the original site at Ellesmere by Eleanor Vachell in 1932, but it has not been seen in that canal again.

In 1899 William Hunt Painter recorded it at Randlay Hay Pool (SJ7008).

The first record for the Montgomery Canal was by Max Walters at Redwith Bridge (SJ2923) in 1955 (conf. Dandy & Taylor, CGE). It was later recorded on the Aston Locks stretch (SJ3326) by John Alder in 1985 and Rashmi Dave in 1986.

The only recent site for it was the Newport Canal (SJ7319), where it was recorded by Chris Walker in 1986 and 1992, and subsequently by Whild & Lockton in 1995. It was probably introduced together with many exotic species when the canal was restored in the 1970s, but the source is not known. It seems to have been lost when the canal started to leak and was re-lined in the late 1990s.

Potamogeton praelongus

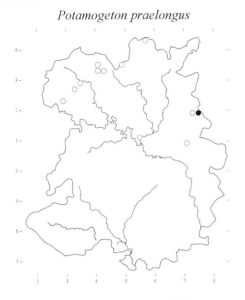

[*Potentilla neumanniana* Reichb.]
Spring Cinquefoil
Not in Shropshire.

There is little reason to believe this was ever a native species in Shropshire. There is just one good record for it, by Edward Williams in about 1800, in the lane between Cound (SJ5505) and Golding (SJ5403). If it was indeed there, it was presumably a casual. It is a plant of bare calcareous habitats such as rock ledges on mountains and coastal cliffs. In the New Atlas it is recorded in just 24 squares in Britain, making it Nationally Scarce. There are also records by Mary McGhie in four places near Ludlow, and one recent one at Llynclys Hill by a Wildlife Trust surveyor in 1993, but these are best considered unconfirmed.

Potentilla rivalis Nutt. Ex Torr. & A. Gray
Brook Cinquefoil
Neophyte. Rare.

The only site for this North American plant in Britain is at Barnsley Pool (SO7592), where it was collected in 1978 by S.R. Price and was last recorded by Joan Brown in 1993.

[*Pyrola media* Sw.]
Intermediate Wintergreen
Not in Shropshire.

The few records that there are of this species in Shropshire are of poor quality and are unsupported by specimens. They give rise to a cluster of dots on the map in the New Atlas that are hundreds of kilometres south of the nearest extant populations, and Fred Rumsey points out that in the past it was over-recorded for the much commoner *Pyrola minor*.

The first record for the county was by Frederick Westcott in 1842, at Whitcliffe Coppice (which is either Whitcliffe Wood, SO4783 or Whitcliffe Common, SO5074). Westcott was not terribly reliable and could easily have made an error (see Oswald's account of him in Sinker's Flora, p. 28). George Jorden recorded it in the Wyre Forest (ca. SO7576) in 1856, but that might not have been in Shropshire. William Phillips apparently collected it at Whitcliffe Wood (SO4873) in 1889 and had the specimen confirmed by Arthur Bennett, but neither Phillips nor Bennett were infallible, and the record should be considered doubtful unless the specimen turns up. Sinker (1985) gives an undated and anonymous record for Stanton Lacy (SO4978), which is probably a misinterpretation of Eleanora Armitage's 1925 record of the following.

Pyrola minor L.
Common Wintergreen
Native. Rare.

In Leighton's Flora of 1841 both Thomas Salwey and Andrew Bloxam recorded *Pyrola minor* at Whitcliffe Wood (SO4873); both were first rate botanists. Salwey also found it in a coppice below Diddlebury Common (SO4886). It was subsequently seen at Whitcliffe by Beckwith (1880), Druce (1892), J. Vacey (1962), and Stan Turner (1971).

George Jorden recorded it in the Wyre Forest (ca. SO7576) in about 1856, but whether on the Shropshire or Worcestershire side of the boundary we do not know. In 1925 Eleanora Armitage recorded it 'near Stanton Lacy' (SO4978). This could have been at The Hope (SO5178) or perhaps it was an oblique reference to the old site at Whitcliffe. When the record was published in the Record of Bare Facts (1926) J.C. Melvill took it upon himself to speculate that *Pyrola media* might also occur in the county, which probably accounts for the spurious record in Sinker's Flora; but there is no suggestion that Armitage recorded it.

L.W. Poel found it at Knowle Wood (SO6073) in the late 1950s, and it was still there in 1987 when Mary Fuller and Henry Hand saw it there. David Stoves recorded it at Oldfield Coppice (SO6089) in 1974 (conf. F.H. Perring). The only recent site for it is at Lydebrook Dingle (SJ6605), where it was found by Whild & Lockton in 1996.

Pyrola minor

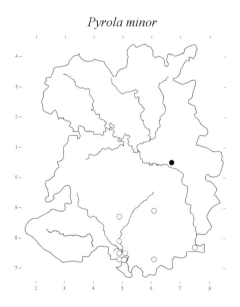

Pyrola rotundifolia L.
Round-leaved Wintergreen
Neophyte. Extinct (1988).

Leighton (1841) gave a record by Henry Spare of this species at Whitcliffe Wood (SO4873), but this is surely another error for *P. minor*. In 1988, however, Roy Mantle discovered it in an abandoned quarry at Poles Coppice (SJ3904), where it did not last more than a few years before the habitat changed due to succession.

Radiola linoides Roth
Allseed
Archaeophyte. Extinct (1939).

This species was once widespread on heavily grazed or disturbed heaths. Edward Williams recorded it at Shawbury Heath (SJ5420) and Uckington Heath (SJ5610) in about 1800. It was still at Shawbury Heath in 1882, when William Beckwith saw it there.

Henry Bidwell collected it at Rudge Heath (SO7995) in 1841 (conf. Leighton). Robert Garner recorded it at Gravenhunger (SJ7342) in 1844. Sinker gives two undated and anonymous records for Priors Halton (SO4975) and Poughnhill (SO5373), which may have come from Hamilton's Flora of 1913. The last record was by J.B. Johnson in 1939 at Haughmond Abbey (SJ5415).

Ranunculus arvensis L.
Corn Buttercup
Archaeophyte. Extinct (1990).

This was once a troublesome weed of cereal crops on heavy, calcareous soils in lowland England, with Shropshire on the north-west edge of its former range. Leighton (1841) described it as 'not very common' and took the trouble to list fifteen sites for it in his Flora. Beckwith listed twelve sites in 1882, but since then there have been just ten records for the county, most recently as a casual in a garden at Wentnor (SO3892, S. & P. Kingsbury, 1990), where it presumably came up from buried seed.

Ranunculus arvensis

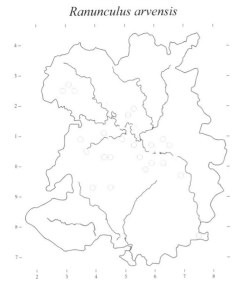

Ranunculus *bachii* Wirtg.
Wirtgen's Water-crowfoot
Native. Extinct (1897).

The identification of river water-crowfoots is very difficult, and records of hybrids (it is not certain whether this would be *fluitans* × *trichophyllus* or *fluitans* × *aquatilis*) are particularly problematic. John Fraser collected what he thought was this (sterile) hybrid in the Severn at Bewdley (SO7875) (in v.c. 40 but modern Worcestershire) in 1883, but J.G. Baker and C.C. Babington disagreed. Painter's specimen from the Severn at Buildwas (SJ6404) in 1897 was confirmed by W.P. Hiern, and seems a perfectly good record.

Ranunculus sardous Crantz
Hairy Buttercup
Archaeophyte. Rare.

This species is best considered an archaeophyte in Shropshire, although in the New Atlas it is treated as a native in coastal regions. Edward Williams recorded it in clover fields and pastures on clay soil, with no specific locality, in about 1800. Leighton (1841) gives records for Albrighton (SJ4918, Elsmere), Ashford (SO5271, McGhie) and Welbatch (SJ4508, T. Bodenham). William Phillips found it still at Welbatch in 1878. Richard Benson collected it in fields near Plealey (SJ4206) in 1892.

Henry Hand found it in his garden at Alcaston (SO4687) in 1971, and it was subsequently recorded on the edges of nearby arable fields (Hand, 1978; H. Davidson, 1990). Frank Perring reported that there were a few plants in a grassy area at Brown Moss (SJ5639) in 1997.

Ranunculus sardous

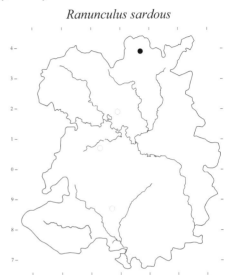

Ranunculus *virzionensis* A. Félix
(*R. aquaticus* × *peltatus*)
Native. Rare.

This rare hybrid water-crowfoot was discovered by Sarah Whild, growing with both parents in a stream on Wild Moor (SO4296) on the Long Mynd in 2003.

Rhynchospora alba (L.) Vahl
White Beak-sedge
Native. Rare.

In Shropshire this species occurs in some of the mosses in the north of the county and in wet heathland around Titterstone Clee. Edward Williams first recorded it at Shomere Moss (SJ5007) in 1798, and it was later found at nearby Bomere (SJ4908) by John Evans in about 1805. Leighton saw it in both those places in the 1830s and William Phillips made similar records in 1878. It was last seen at Shomere by Beckwith in 1880.

Williams also first recorded it at The Mere, Ellesmere (SJ4034) in about 1800, and it was also seen there by Andrew Bloxam in 1841. It was probably in the bog known as The Moors at the south end of the mere. This site was largely drained during the construction of the Ellesmere Canal in about 1800, as was Rednal Moss (SJ3427), where Williams also found it in 1800, and Leighton later recorded it in 1841.

The first record for Whixall Moss (SJ4936) was by J.E. Bowman in 1841. It has since been recorded there many times, including by Beckwith in 1880, E.A. Wilson in 1949, Sinker in 1962, Trueman in 1984, Perring in 1989, and lastly by Pat Parker in 1994. The last place it was recorded in was by the side of the canal, but when the leak was fixed in the 1990s the *Rhynchospora* soon disappeared, and it has not yet returned to the main part of the moss in response to the restoration works. At nearby Wem Moss (SJ4734) it was first recorded by Rose & Bellamy in 1959, and has since been recorded many times. In 2004 it was still quite frequent in wet hollows on the north-west side of the moss (Lockton).

George Jorden recorded it at 'Oreton, Farlow and adjacent parts' in 1856. This is probably a reference to Catherton Common (SO6478), where J.B. Duncan found it in 1903. John Bingham later found it at Titterstone Clee (SO5975) in 1990 – just one small clump.

Rhynchospora alba

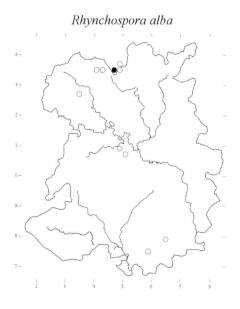

William Beckwith discovered it at Clarepool Moss (SJ4334) in 1880, where it has since been recorded by Diamond (1891), Rose & Bellamy (1959), Sinker (1961), Keith Bell (1976), Walker (1980) and Andrew Hearle (1987).

The records above seem to show that it favours mosses that are in the process of drying out, but it soon disappears when the mire becomes scrubbed over. On Wem Moss it occurs in tiny fragments of M18 *Erica tetralix-Sphagnum papillosum* mire, and it is also found on M2 *Sphagnum fallax* lawns.

Rosa spinosissima L.
Burnet Rose
Native. Rare.

In Shropshire this plant occurs on limestone rock exposures and cliffs. Arthur Aikin was the first to record it in the county, at Llanymynech Hill (SJ2622) in 1796. It was not recorded there again until 1970, when Doris Pugh found it along the path above Blodwel Rocks (SJ2623), and Ruth Dawes reported that there was one plant still remaining in 1999.

In about 1800 Edward Williams found it by the side of the road near Snailbeach (SJ3702). Leighton (1841) gives records by Mary McGhie for Ludlow Racecourse (SO4977) and by W. Watkins for Shotton Hall (SJ4922). George Jorden recorded it in the Wyre Forest (ca. SO7576) in 1856, and George Druce found it at Quatford (SO7390) in 1911.

In 1970 Doris Pugh also recorded it at Bryn Celyn (SJ2525), where it was later seen by Peter Benoit (1987) and was still flourishing in 2003 (Dawes, Whild & Lockton). This may be the only native site for it left in the county.

Bryan Fowler found it on a roadside wall at Pickstock (SJ7223) in 1976, where it was presumably an introduction, as was the plant that Tavia MacLean recorded at Newport (SJ7519) in 1981 and 1986.

Rubus saxatilis L.
Stone Bramble
Native. Extinct (1991)

Littleton Brown recorded this species at Combe Floyd (presumably Cwm Ffrydd, SO2586) in 1725 and Arthur Aikin saw it on the Stiperstones (ca. SO3698) in about 1805, but it has not been recorded at either of those sites again. Sinker claims that it was first recorded at Craig Sychtyn (SJ2325) in 1866, but does not say who the finder was. It has since been recorded there by Diamond (who called the site Trefonen) in 1891, Ian Bonner in 1969, Graham Walker in 1988 and Rob Stokes in 1991. There are no voucher specimens for any of these records and recent searches have been unsuccessful.

Sinker also gives a record for the Wyre Forest (ca. SO7576) but without date or recorder, and Ian Bonner made a tentative record for Nantmawr Quarry (SJ2524) in 1969.

Sagina nodosa (L.) Fenzl
Knotted Pearlwort
Native. Scarce.

Leighton considered this species to be rare in Shropshire, and gave just three records of it. Edward Williams had recorded it on Haughmond Hill (SJ5414) in about 1800; Thomas Salwey had seen it somewhere near Oswestry (ca. SJ2929) in about 1841; and John Bowman had found it at Crose Mere (SJ4230). It is a plant of calcareous flushes and wet grassland, and it has declined dramatically in lowland England in recent decades, although it is still common in upland areas and the north.

At Crose Mere it has since been recorded by Beckwith (1882), Mackenzie (1958), Sinker (1960), Keith Bell (1976), Wigginton (1979), Walker (1980-1990) and Rob Stokes (1993). It used to occur in the fen on the south-east shore, but it disappeared when this area was fenced off and turned to scrub. However, it reappeared in a different place in 2003 (Lockton), following the introduction of a suitably light grazing regime in the fields to the north.

Beckwith (1882 & 1889) also found it at Cole Mere (SJ4333), Rednal (SJ3527) and Weston Lullingfields (SJ4224). In the latter two sites it was associated with the canal. Richard Benson found it at Pulverbatch (SJ4202) in 1894. John Ramsbottom recorded it at Blake Mere (SJ4133) in 1907, when William Painter also saw it at Highley (SJ7483). Oswald Feilden's record for Frankton (SJ3633) in 1920 could have been for the canal or for one of various meres and mosses.

The first record of it in an upland situation was by Ellen Heywood-Waddington at Titterstone Clee (SO6078) in 1978. It has since been seen there by Pat Waite (SO5977, 1982), John Bingham (SO6079 & SO6175, 1988), Kate Thorne (SO5977, 1999). It has also been recorded on Brown Clee Hill (SO5885 & SP5985, Mary Fuller, 1979); on the Long Mynd (SO4392, Helen Davidson, 1978 & SO4294, Trueman, 1990); and on Stapeley Hill (SO3199, Walker, 1990).

The first record for Trefonen Marshes (SJ2426) was by Doris Pugh in 1979, and it has since been recorded there by Margaret Deadman (1990), Pat Parker & Ruth Dawes (1992), Rob Stokes (1993), and Walker, Wrench, Whild & Lockton in 1995. In 1997 John Bingham, Mark Lawley and John Clayfield found a new site at Overton Common (SO4971) in 1997.

Sagina nodosa

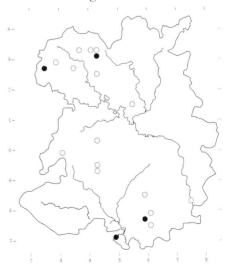

Sagittaria sagittifolia L

Arrowhead

Native. Rare.

Shropshire is on the very western edge of the range of this species, which is typical of slow-flowing calcareous rivers and canals. It occurs in the Severn below Shrewsbury and in the lower reaches of the Tern and Roden, but has not been recorded in any other site for some time.

In 1800 Edward Williams considered it to be so common in ponds and ditches that he did not specify any localities at all. Joseph Babington, in 1803, described it as 'plentiful in ditches and pools' around Ludlow (SO5174). Leighton (1841) considered it to be 'not uncommon,' and gave records for Eyton on the Weald Moors (SJ6514, Eyton), Crudgington (SJ6517, Bidwell) and Ludlow (SO5175, McGhie). He and Charles Babington collected it in the Shrewsbury Canal (SJ5114) in 1832, and Leighton saw it in a pit at Uffington (SJ5213).

Of these early sites, it was later recorded at the Weald Moors by R. Anslow in 1865 and by Beckwith in 1880, but it has not been seen there since. There are records for the Shrewsbury canal by Phillips (1878 & 1894), Beckwith (1880) and Norah Mackenzie (1946 & 1950), but no recent ones. It has never been recorded in the Ludlow area again.

Beckwith found it at Sundorne Pool (SJ5215) and in the River Tern (ca. SJ5509) in 1880. It has subsequently been recorded in the Tern again many times (e.g. Whild & Lockton, 2004) but always in the lowermost reaches. If it is present further upstream the current might be too strong to allow it to develop floating or emergent leaves.

The first record for the River Severn was by Potts & Allen in 1901, who considered it to be plentiful from Shrewsbury (SJ4912) to Bridgnorth (SO7192). If so, there have not been many records. J.B. Duncan had it at Highley (SO7483) in 1903; J.W. Heath saw it at Atcham (SJ5308) in 1911; M.H. Bigwood recorded it at Coalport (SJ7002) in 1953; Pat Parker found it at Cound (SJ5705 & SJ5605) in 1981; and Joanna Deacon recorded it at Wroxeter (SJ5608), where it still was in 1996

(Whild & Lockton). There are, however, quite a few unlocalised tetrad records that are undoubtedly for the Severn (e.g. John Box, SJ60R, 1993), which suggests that Potts & Allen's account still holds true.

It has not fared so well in the canals. It was found in the Newport Canal (SJ6915) by W.H. Painter in 1907 but was last seen there in 1993 (T. MacLean, SJ7319).

It was first recorded in the Roden (SJ5524) by Mrs E. Kirkham in 1964, and was present at Ercall Mill (SJ5816), Roden (SJ5616) and Poynton (SJ5717) in 1995 (Lockton).

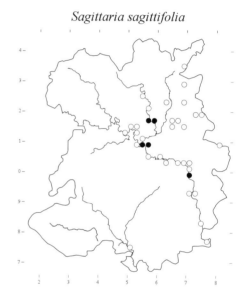

Sagittaria sagittifolia

Salix myrsinifolia Salisb.

Dark-leaved Willow

Neophyte. Extinct (1982).

This species was apparently recorded on Shawbury Heath (SJ5420, Anon.) in 1946. Sinker found a plant at Merrington Green (SJ4621) in 1982, which was probably planted there. It had gone by 1995.

Salix purpurea L.

Purple Willow

Native. Scarce.

This species seems to occur as a native around some of the meres and, possibly, along some rivers, although it has also been widely planted for centuries.

Edward Williams recorded it in about 1800 at Eaton Mascott (SJ5305), where it was probably planted in hedges. Leighton collected it at Alkmund Park Pool (SJ4912) in about 1841, where it has since been recorded by Phillips in 1878 and by Wigginton in 1979. This seems likely to be a native site for it.

(SJ4329), and Whittington (SJ3231). Williams also knew of it at Rednal Moss (SJ3427), where it was recorded by a Dr Smith. Leighton saw it at Shawbury Heath in about 1841, and in 1891 Diamond listed it for Glopa (SJ2631), but it has never been recorded in any of these sites again.

Salix purpurea

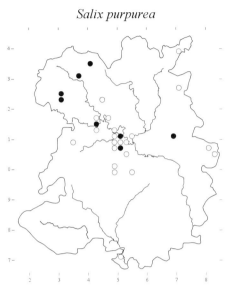

Salix repens

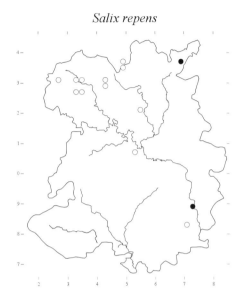

Other meres where it has been recorded include Betton Pool (SJ5107, Wigginton, 1979 & Walker, 1980); Bomere Pool (SJ5008, Pat Parker, 1978; Wigginton, 1979; Whild & Lockton, 2003); Marton Pool, Baschurch (SJ4423, C. Fuller & P. Richards, 1968; Wigginton 1980); Mere Pool (SJ5110, Sinker, 1980; Whild & Lockton, 1996-2003); Morton Pool (SJ3023, Hearle & Walker, 1986; Whild & Lockton, 2003); and The Mere, Ellesmere (SJ4035, Wigginton, 1979; Whild & Lockton, 1997-2003). In other sites it is probably planted.

Salix repens L.
Creeping Willow
Native. Rare.

This species was once characteristic of the meres and mosses, but it has now declined almost to extinction in the county, with just one extant site known.

It was first recorded by Edward Williams in about 1800 at Berrington (SJ5306), Shawbury Heath (SJ5420), Stocket Moor

In recent times it has only been recorded at three sites: Crose Mere (SJ4330), Whixall Moss (SJ4936) and Betton Moss (SJ6836). At Crose Mere it was discovered by Sinker in 1970 and was later seen by Walker (1986) and Hearle (1989), but it seems to have gone from there. Sinker also discovered it at Whixall Moss in 1962, and Trueman saw it there as recently as 1994, but like several other species it might have been flooded out as a result of the recent attempts at restoration. The only site at which it persists is Betton Moss, where Paul Bell discovered it in 1977. There were initially many plants, but that had declined to just three by 2001 (Bell).

This species is also planted at the Shropshire Wildlife Trust's Chelmarsh reserve (SO7288, A.K. Thorne, 2001).

Salvia pratensis L.
Meadow Clary
Archaeophyte. Extinct (1841).

Leighton rejected Henry Spare's record of this species at Oakly Park (SO4876), but when William Brookes collected a specimen on the roadside at Fox Farm (SJ5209, 1841) he gave it the benefit of the doubt and included it in the additions to his Flora. It has been a common garden plant in Britain for centuries, and has no claim to be native in Shropshire.

Salvia verbenaca L.
Wild Clary
Archaeophyte. Extinct (1944).

Although it is considered to be native in the south-east of England, this species only seems to occur in Shropshire in places where it has probably been sown. Edward Williams recorded it near St. Mary's (SJ4912) and St. Giles's (SJ5011) churches in Shrewsbury in about 1800. It was still in the hedge at St. Giles's when Leighton saw it in 1841 and when Phillips saw it in 1878. Beckwith found it at Bridgnorth (SO7192), Harnage (SJ5604) and Cross Houses (SJ5307) in the 1880s. It was still at Bridgnorth in 1902 when it was seen by G.A. Audley, in 1911 when Druce saw it on rocks below the castle, and in 1944 when it was recorded by R.S. Lucas.

In Diamond's Flora of Oswestry of 1891 it is listed for Llanymynech (SJ2620), which may have been interpreted as Llanymynech Hill by Eric Hardy in an article for Shropshire Magazine in 1970. It seems more likely to have been in the churchyard.

The only recent record is by John Martin, who found it on a roadside at Monkmoor (SJ5011) in 1990, where it was introduced in a seed mix by the County Council.

Samolus valerandi L.
Brookweed
Native. Rare.

Thomas Salwey recorded this species at Trefonen (SJ2526) in 1841. Diamond listed it for Welsh Frankton (SJ3633) in his Flora of 1891, and Oswald Feilden (who probably made the previous record) recorded it at The Mere, Ellesmere (SJ4034) in 1920. George Druce found it 'in great plenty' on the county boundary with Staffordshire between Newport and Aqualate (SJ7519) in 1925.

Sinker found it at Crose Mere (SJ4330) in 1968.

In recent times it has been recorded at just three sites – all drainage ditches in agricultural areas: Pat Parker found it at Bromley Fen (SJ3925 & SJ4025) in 1983, where it persisted until 1986 (Parker); John Box found it at Crudgington Moor (SJ6417) in 1990, where it lasted until 1992 (Jean Rapson); and Kate Thorne found it near Welsh Frankton (SJ3432) in 2001, where it still was in 2002 (Thorne).

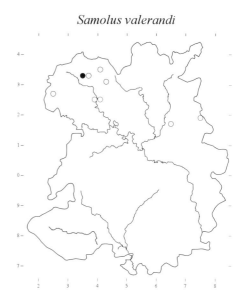

Samolus valerandi

Sanguisorba officinalis L.
Great Burnet
Native. Rare.

The earliest known record of this species in Shropshire was by R.G. Higgins, who found it growing by the side of the Newport Canal near Edgmond (SJ7118) in about 1832. It was presumably a casual there. In 1835 William Anstice recorded it at 'Cheshire's Upper Meadow,' which is an unknown locality, possibly near Cheshire Coppice (SJ6213).

Leighton (1841) listed it at Lord's Meadows (SJ8203), where George Lloyd found it, and it has since been recorded by Bryan Fowler (1976), Ian Trueman (1984), Dan Wrench (1995) and Whild & Lockton (1997). This is one of the few examples of an MG4 *Alopecurus pratensis-Sanguisorba officinalis* grassland in the county.

Also in Leighton's Flora is a record by Henry Spare for Oakly Park (SO4876), which should be treated as unconfirmed. George Jorden's 1856 record for the Wyre Forest (ca. SO7576) is more likely to be for Worcestershire.

William Beckwith found it in a meadow by a small brook above Cruckton Hall (SJ4310) in 1889, and in 1991 Diamond listed it for Welshampton (SJ4334).

In 1892 William Phillips recorded it on a roadside near Marton (SJ2802), and in 1898 Richard Benson and W. Yelland recorded it at Marton Pool, Chirbury (SJ2902). J.K. Rodwell also listed it for that site in 1982, and Joyce Roper recorded it on a roadside near Chirbury (SO2698), in a ditch near Marrington (SO2697), and on a hedgebank near Sidnal (SO2696) in 1981.

Frances Pitt recorded it at Westwood (SO7091) in 1911 and 1912.

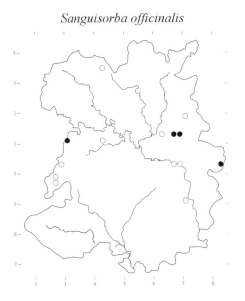

Sanguisorba officinalis

Bill Thompson's record for a railway line at Coalport (SJ6902) in 1982 is presumably of a casual or a garden escape. John Box recorded it as established on a nature reserve in Ironbridge (SJ6703) in 1982, where it was originally sown.

In 1995 it was discovered in a development site on the Weald Moors at Hortonwood (SJ6813, Whild & Lockton), where it grew in ditches and old grassland. Assuming it has

gone from the Chirbury area, this is therefore only the second native site for it in the county. A recent record for the tetrad SJ31A is of a garden escape on a roadside verge (Hoare, Knowles & Cutler, 2003).

Saxifraga hypnoides L.
Mossy Saxifrage
Native. Extinct (1842).

It is not known who first discovered this upland plant still surviving on Titterstone Clee (SO5977). There are records from about 1800 by Edward Williams, Arthur Aikin and Joseph Babington. The latter noted that it was commonly grown in gardens, but clearly considered the plants on Titterstone Clee to be wild. Edwin Lees and Henry Spare recorded it in Leighton's Flora of 1841, and Fred Westcott reported that it was abundant at Hoar Edge (SO6077) in 1842. George Jorden confirmed that it was on the summit of Titterstone Clee in 1856, but there are no records of it there since then.

Bryan Fowler found it growing as a garden escape in Boningale (SJ8202) in 1979, but it did not last long. In 1983 R. Tapper, from the Nature Conservancy Council, recorded it (apparently in error) on the Long Mynd (SO4191).

Scandix pecten-veneris L.
Shepherd's-needle
Archaeophyte. Extinct (1954).

This was once a common agricultural weed, and neither Edward Williams (ca. 1800) nor William Leighton (ca. 1841) gave any specific records for it because it was too common to record. By the 1880s, however, Beckwith found it scarce enough to mention that it was 'not unfrequent' in cornfields at Minsterley (SJ3705) and around Sharpstones Hill (SJ4909). Diamond also found it to be fairly common near Oswestry (ca. SJ2929) in 1891. William Phillips recorded it at Wigley (SJ3708) in 1983. By this time it must have been quite rare, because Richard Benson and W. Yelland made a note of it at Leigh Hall (SJ3303) in 1898, and George Potts recorded it growing 'plentifully' in a field above Edge Wood (SJ6101) in 1929. It may have been in the same place on Wenlock Edge that he and the Reverend Sequeira recorded it in 1933. In 1954 G.D. Adams found it at Bishops Castle (SO3288), but there have been no records of it in the wild since then. Alan Feest recorded it as a bird seed alien at Bushmoor (SO4387) in 1976, and Sylvia Kingsbury had it come up in a new garden in Wentnor (SO3892) in 1994, presumably from buried seed.

Scheuchzeria palustris L.
Rannoch-rush
Native. Extinct (1884).

The significance of Rannoch-rush in Britain is as a glacial relic, and although there are only nine sites in Britain where it survived until modern times, its remains occur in most lowland raised mires not far below the surface. This is not a rare plant, globally. It is one of the dominant species over thousands, possibly millions of square miles of bog in subarctic regions. It is not even a rare plant in Britain, with hundreds of thousands of plants on Rannoch Moor, but it is now restricted to that one site. It was Babington who first discovered *Scheuchzeria palustris* in Shropshire in 1831 although, as Leighton points out, the schoolmaster John Jeudwine collected it seven years earlier without appreciating the significance of what he had found. Babington's site was a bog on the west side of Bomere Pool (SJ4908), and Leighton later recorded it from the nearby Shomere Moss (SJ5007). The last known record for Bomere was in 1881, when William Beckwith and the Reverend W.M.D. La Touche found only a few plants. The other sites where it has been recorded are Clarepool Moss (SJ4334, O.M. Feilden, 1866), and the Mere at Ellesmere (SJ4034, Beckwith, 1884).

Schoenoplectus tabernaemontani (C.C. Gmel.) Palla
Grey Club-rush
Native. Scarce.

Lloyd & Rutter (1957) reported a record of this species at White Mere (SJ4132) by William Phillips in 1888. At that time it must have seemed an unlikely record, but it has since been recorded there by Frank Perring

(1975), Keith Bell (1977), Martin Wigginton (1979) and Chris Walker (1985 & 1990).

A second site, at Crose Mere (SJ4330), was discovered by Charles Sinker in 1960, and it has since been recorded there by J.M. Way (1963), Sinker (1969), Wigginton (1979) and Whild & Lockton (2003).

Schoenoplectus tabernaemontani

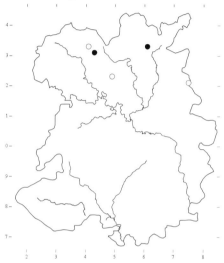

Mrs B. Potter recorded it in a pond at Newton on the Hill (SJ4823) in 1975, and it was still there in 1986 (V. Jones & P. Parker). Trina Paskell recorded it in the River Meese at Chetwynd (SJ7421) in 1981, and Julie Edwards found it in a pond at Aychley Farm (SJ6033) in 1997 (conf. Walker & Whild).

Scleranthus annuus ssp. polycarpos (L.) Bonnier & Layens
Scarce Annual Knawel
Native. Rare.

There are only three records of this plant in the county, although it might well be overlooked. It seems to occur in U1 *Festuca ovina-Agrostis capillaris-Rumex acetosella* grassland, which is still quite widespread in the county.

Charles Babington collected a specimen at Bayston Hill (SJ4808) in 1837 (conf. P.D. Sell, CGE), and Charles Sinker found it at Kempsters Hill (SJ3114) in 1978 (conf. Sell).

Sinker also accepted a record by Joyce Roper for Middleton Hall Farm (SO2999, 1982).

Sedum forsterianum Smith
Rock Stonecrop
Native. Scarce.

This plant occurs on dry rock outcrops and stabilised screes, and is sometimes found established on walls and quarry ledges. It is described by Lynne Farrell in *Scarce Plants* as also growing in wet woodlands, but that does not appear to be the case in Shropshire. It is now very widely established throughout Britain and Ireland, and has a total of 390 current dots in the New Atlas. The authors admit that it is now impossible to distinguish native from introduced populations.

In Shropshire there are a few sites where it has long been recorded. Littleton Brown found it at Bury Ditches (SO3284) in 1726, and Edwin Lees recorded it still there about 100 years later, but it has not been seen since. Joseph Babington recorded it on Titterstone Clee (SO5977) in 1803, and George Jorden also saw it there in 1856, growing amongst the scree, but again it seems to have gone. William Leighton (1841) recorded it in three places: at Haughmond Hill (SJ5414), where it has not been seen again; at Caer Caradoc (SO4795), where Francis Dickinson also saw it at about the same time; and at Earl's Hill (SJ4004), where it has been seen many times subsequently, most recently by Sarah Whild in 2002.

The Long Mynd (SO4293) is another site with a long history of recording. Thomas Salwey and Francis Dickinson recorded it there in Leighton's Flora, and it was also seen by William Beckwith in 1880. William Hunt Painter recorded it in Light Spout Hollow (SO4395) in 1897, and W.E. Thompson saw it in 1904. Curiously, it was missed at this site during Sinker's Flora project, but in 1996 a team from the National Trust found it in Ashes Hollow (SO4393), Minton Batch (SO4191) and Sleekstonebank Hollow (SO4291). Since then John Clayfield and Kate Thorne have found it in five locations along the eastern flanks of the hill.

Sedum forsterianum

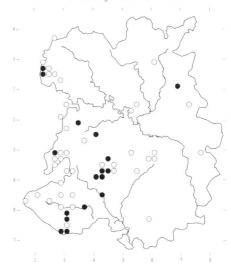

Other sites for this species include The Lump, Priestweston (SO2928), where it was first recorded by Joyce Roper in 1980 and most recently by Chris Walker in 1994; Craig Sychtyn (SJ2325), where Stan Turner found it in 1968, and it was last seen by Ruth Dawes in 2000; and Hazler Hill near Church Stretton (SO4693), where W.E. Thompson found it in 1904, and it was still present during Sinker's Flora project in about 1984. More recently discovered native sites for it include Bulthy Bank, on the Shropshire side of Craig Breidden (SJ3114), where it was found in 1992; Coed-detton (SO2973, S.J. Whild, 1999), Pentre Hill (SO3176, Whild, 1995), Rock of Woolbury (SO3179, J. Clayfield, 1992), Stapeley Hill (SO3098, C. Walker, 1994), and Whittery Wood (SO2798, Whild, 1997).

Presumably it should be considered an introduction in such places as Badger (SO7699, O.M. Feilden, 1910), Callaughton (SO6197, 1841, W.P. Brookes), Hodnet (SJ6129, E.N. Rutter, 1962), Wistanstow (SO4385, Whild, 1995), Tibberton (SJ6820, Lockton, 1997) and Westbury Churchyard (SJ3509, Whild, 1996).

[*Selaginella selaginoides* (L.) Link]
Lesser Clubmoss
Not in Shropshire.

The only record of this species in Shropshire was by Griffith Griffiths in about 1870, who considered it to be abundant on the Long Mynd (ca. SO4293) in about 1870. He was almost certainly mistaken.

[*Senecio cambrensis* Rosser]
Welsh Ragwort
Not in Shropshire.

In 1970 *Senecio cambrensis* was believed to be expanding its range, as several new sites had just been discovered in north Wales. Douglas Kent made a casual observation that he had seen it at Oswestry and Ludlow, and these 'records' found their way into the botanical literature. They were, however, never supported by voucher specimens nor repeated, so it seems Kent might have been mistaken.

Serratula tinctoria L.
Saw-wort
Native. Rare.

Leighton (1841) gives four records of this species, at Astley (SJ5218, E. Elsmere), Chesterton Roman Camp (SO7896, G. Lloyd), Whitcliffe (SO5074, Spare) and the Wyre Forest (SO7576, Jorden). G.H. Griffiths recorded it at Willstone (SO4995) in 1870; H. Auden found it on Haughmond Hill (SJ5414) in 1882; Beckwith saw it in the Wyre Forest again in 1882; W.H. Painter recorded it on The Wrekin (SJ6308) in 1906; and J.C. Melvill found it at Badger Dingle (SO7799) in 1913. H.E. Forrest recorded it there and at Marrington Dingle (SO2797) in 1914.

In 1961 E.M. Rutter recorded it in the Wyre Forest again, and in 1976 and 1977 Malcolm Clark and John Bingham mapped its distribution there, finding it in the squares SO7376, SO7476, SO7576, SO7676 & SO7677. Also in 1977 Chris Walker discovered it at The Hollies, Ticklerton (SO4891) and Joyce Roper found it at Hobarris Wood (SO3077). It still occurs at

these two sites, with recent sightings at The Hollies by Dan Wrench in 1994, and at Hobarris Wood by John Clayfield in 2003.

Mary Fuller found a new site at Sutton Hill (SO5382) in 1980, but it was gone from there by 1986. John Bingham discovered a population at Sturt Common (SO7278) in 1997. It remains present, but apparently declining, in the Wyre Forest near the Dowles Brook, in 2004 (J. & D. Bingham).

Serratula tinctoria

Silene conica L.
Sand Catchfly
Neophyte. Extinct (1987).

In 1987 one plant of this species appeared on the verge of the new Oswestry bypass (SJ2927, M. Wainwright), presumably as an introduced casual. It has not been recorded again.

Silene gallica L.
Small-flowered Catchfly
Neophyte. Extinct (1987).

This is typically a species of free-draining, acidic, sandy arable fields and heaths, especially by the coast. In Shropshire it seems to be a recent introduction and has only ever been recorded along roadsides near the A5 Holyhead Road. E.M. Rutter and H.M. Bigwood first found it in a field gateway at Knockin Heath (SJ3521) in 1959, and it has since been seen in the vicinity by Sinker (1970) and E.D. Pugh (1979). Marjorie Wainwright found some plants on the newly-constructed Oswestry bypass (SJ3028) in 1987. This species is best considered a neophyte in Shropshire, although there is a distant possibility that the plants were actually from long-buried seed.

Silene noctiflora L.
Night-flowering Catchfly
Archaeophyte. Extinct (1959).

This is a former agricultural weed, which was once common in the south-east of England, with Shropshire somewhat beyond the edge of its range. In 1894 O.M. Feilden found two or three plants in a field near Halston (SJ3431), and he reported them again in 1920, but possibly this was just the old record being repeated. Hamilton found it in a fallow field at Bayston Hill (SJ4808) in 1894. George Potts found it in a disused chicken run at Tickwood (SJ6402) in 1929 and Edward Rutter recorded it at Hodnet (SJ6129) in 1956. The last record of it as an archaeophyte was in 1959, when Francis Rose and Charles Sinker found it in a field at Welshampton (SJ4233). Elizabeth Roberts found four plants as garden throw-outs at Oswestry Racecourse (SJ2531) in 1992.

Silene nutans L.
Nottingham Catchfly
Neophyte. Rare.

The evidence for this species being native in Shropshire is rather thin. It was recorded at Hawkstone Park by William Wood in Turner & Dillwyn's Botanist's Guide of 1805. Wood was not a Shropshire botanist, and he might well have a been a visitor, come to see the follies that Richard Hill had constructed there. It seems rather patronising to suggest that gardeners in the 18th century could not have introduced this commonly-cultivated plant, but the fact that it has become established at this site, and persists to this day (O'Donnell, 1995) is of some interest. A record of it at Apley Terrace (SO7297) by William Anstice in about 1835 is either a mistake or perhaps another introduction at a country estate.

[Sium latifolium L.]
Greater Water-parsnip
Not in Shropshire

There is no good evidence for this species ever occurring in Shropshire. William Penny Brookes (1841) reported it at Wenlock Abbey (SJ6200), but he may have been mistaken. The habitat seems unlikely, and there is no corroborating evidence. There were two dots for it in Shropshire in the 1962 Atlas (SJ32 & SJ43), which were queried by Sinker, but one of them, attributed to Allan McGregor Stirling in 1956, is given in the New Atlas as an introduction. We are not aware of any such introduction attempt, and it seems more likely that it was simply an identification error.

T.E. Mitchell's 1980 record for a 'damp bank near Clun,' given in Sinker's Flora, is also an obvious error. One reason for this species being so over-recorded may be that some plants of Apium nodiflorum do grow exceptionally large and could be mistaken for it. But Sium is very different in growth form and has more specific habitat requirements, so it seems best to disregard all the records for it in Shropshire.

Sorbus anglica Hedlund
English Whitebeam
Native. Rare.

It was Ellen Lloyd who first noticed the unusual whitebeams at Llynclys Hill (SJ2723) in 1926, but J.C. Melvill concluded that they were S. rupicola. In 1955 E.F. Warburg also recorded S. rupicola at Blodwel Rocks (SJ2623). It was apparently not until 1972 when Kathleen Saville collected specimens at Blodwel Rocks that the S. anglica was properly identified. Saville counted 25 trees along the escarpment; in 1986 Ruth Dawes counted just 16; but in 1987 Vicky Morgan made the total 51. She also counted five on Llynclys Hill. Doris Pugh discovered one small tree in the Llanymynech Rocks reserve in 1974. It was later cut down by a conservation working group, but it recovered and Ruth Dawes has suggested that it might in fact be *S. aria*. There remains a high degree of uncertainty about the identification and abundance of the whitebeams at Llanymynech Rocks, Blodwel Rocks and Llynclys Hill, where *Sorbus aria* and possibly *S. rupicola* also occur.

Sorbus domestica L.
Service-tree
Neophyte. Rare.

John Bingham found five trees of this species in Withybed Wood (SO7576) in 1979, and noted that they were still there in 1991. Ignoring tradition, he made no claim that they are anything other than planted. There is no reason to consider it native anywhere in Britain, but it needs to be listed here as a species with an extensive mythology.

[*Sorbus rupicola* (Syme) Hedl.]
Rock Whitebeam
Not in Shropshire.

When Ellen Lloyd first noticed the unusual whitebeams on Llynclys Hill in 1926, J.C. Melvill suggested that they might be *Pyrus aria* var. *rupicola* Syme, but they eventually turned out to be *S. anglica*. E.F. Warburg recorded *S. rupicola* on Blodwel Rocks (SJ2623) in 1955, but it seems he might have been mistaken, too. There is therefore no evidence for this species in the county.

Sparganium natans L.
Least Bur-reed
Native. Extinct (1985).

Edward Williams recorded this species in a ditch on Shomere Moss (SJ5007) and in the stretch of the Montgomery canal that runs through Rednal Moss (SJ3427) in about 1800. It is listed in Turner & Dillwyn (1805) as occurring in a large bog at Belmont (SJ3035) which has long since been drained.

In 1835 J.E. Bowman recorded it at The Mere, Ellesmere (SJ4034) and on the north-west margin of Cole Mere (SJ4233) at about the same time. Leighton (1841) recorded it at Hencott Pool (SJ4916) and in ditches north of Bomere Pool (SJ4908). William Phillips gave

the same sites as Leighton in 1878, but added Hencote Rifle Range to the former, which implies that he did really see it there and was not just repeating the old records. In 1880 William Beckwith found it in a pool near Eaton Constantine (SJ5906).

Since then there has only been one site for it in the county. It was discovered at Brown Moss (SJ5639) by Edward Rutter in 1955, and was later recorded by Sinker in 1961 & 1978, by Trueman in 1983 and by Chris Walker in 1981 & 1985. It was in pool 5, which dried up in the 1990s after becoming very overgrown.

Sparganium natans

[*Stellaria nemorum* L.]
Wood Stitchwort
Local status uncertain.

There are no really convincing records of this species in Shropshire. Thomas Salwey, who was usually reliable, recorded it somewhere 'near Oswestry' (SJ22, SJ23, SJ32 or SJ33) in 1841. R.G. Higgins recorded it at Lilleshall Abbey (SJ7314) at about the same time. Mary McGhie's 1841 records for fields near the Teme at Ludlow (SO5075) seem dubious.

Sinker (1985) gives an 1877 record for 'Sharpstones, Cardington' (presumably ca. SO4993) but the recorder is unknown. In 1901 A.R. Horwood listed it for Marrington (SO2796). In 1950 Edward Wilson recorded it at Emberton's Wood, Ellesmere, but we don't know where that is.

It is given post-1930 dots for SO28, SO37 & SO38 in Perring & Walters's Atlas of the British Flora (1962), but no details were ever collected. One record for the Hinstock area (SJ6827), collected for Sinker's Flora project, was never published; and one more recent one collected during the BSBI Monitoring Scheme in 1988 should also be rejected.

In conclusion, there is little evidence that this species has ever occurred in the county, although some of the sites listed do seem quite suitable, ecologically.

Stellaria palustris Retz.
Marsh Stitchwort
Native. Rare.

The sites where this species occurs in Shropshire are mostly either meres or alongside the River Severn. Edward Williams recorded it at Marton Pool, Chirbury (SJ2902) and Cole Mere (SJ4333) in about 1800. In 1841 Bloxam found it at Blake Mere (SJ4133) and Leighton recorded it at the north end of Ellesmere (SJ4035). William Beckwith found it in a ditch at Attingham Park (SJ5510) and at Ellesmere again in 1880.

Stellaria palustris

Sinker found it still at Marton Pool, Chirbury, in 1964, but it has not been recorded there again. Will Prestwood was the first to find it in the floodplain of the Severn at Loton Park (SJ3516) in 1978. It has since been recorded

there by Sarah Stafford (1979) and Chris Walker (1988), but it seems to have gone from there now. The only current site for it is by the Severn at Ford (SJ4214), where Kate Thorne discovered it in 2002, and found it still present in very small quantities in 2004.

Subularia aquatica L.
Awlwort
Native. Extinct (1805).

There is only one record ever of this species in lowland England, at Hencott Pool (SJ4916) in about 1805, by Arthur Aikin. It is species of oligotrophic lakes, and is not uncommon in Wales, Scotland and the Lake District. Although Aikin made a few mistakes (see Oswald in Sinker's Flora, p. 18) he was generally a reliable botanist and he made many important early records. It is evident that *Subularia aquatica* would once have occurred in the Shropshire meres, and at Hencott Pool it was recorded as growing with such species as *Sparganium natans*, *Baldellia ranunculoides*, *Utricularia vulgaris* and *Luronium natans* – precisely the sort of associates that would be expected. On balance it seems best to follow Turner & Dillwyn (1805) and Watson (1835) in accepting this record as another example of a glacial relic surviving in the meres until recent times.

Thalictrum flavum L.
Common Meadow-rue
Native. Rare.

Shropshire is on the edge of the range for this species, which is quite common in the English lowlands but is almost absent from Wales and Scotland. It occurs in base-rich unimproved damp grassland and along ditches and rivers.

Most records for Shropshire are from the floodplain of the Severn or its major tributaries. The localities along the Severn, working downstream, were Nesscliffe Camp (SJ3715, Sarah Stafford, 1976), Underdale (SJ5013, Williams, 1800), Cronkhill (SJ5308, Williams, 1800 & Phillips, 1878), Leighton (SJ6004, Beckwith, 1880), Buildwas (SJ6404, Brookes det. Leighton, 1841 &

Beckwith, 1880), Bridgnorth (SO7192, Beckwith, 1880) and Arley (SO7580, Bill Thompson, 1979 & 1981).

On the Tern it was recorded at Duncote (SJ5711) by Williams in about 1800 and at Attingham Park (SJ5509) by Phillips (1878), Beckwith (1880 & 1883), and Rutter (1955). Dorothy Evans and Joan Connell found it by the Rea Brook at Meole Brace (SJ4810) in 1970, and Sarah Stafford recorded it near the Weir Brook at Melverley (SJ3417) in 1978. In 1933 and 1941 Ellen Lloyd found it near the headwaters of the River Perry at Ebnal (SJ3134).

In 1892 G.R. Jebb found it by the Roden a mile and a half below Wem, and in 1918 he described the locality as 'a wood about two miles below Wem.' The most likely site is Soulton Wood (SJ5429). In 1979 Veronica Jones and Mrs B.E.H. Potter discovered it in field by the Roden above Wem (SJ4928), in a site later bought by the Wildlife Trust and named Ruewood Pastures. *Thalictrum flavum* has steadily declined in abundance there, and is now restricted to one ditch, where it was fenced off to protect it from grazing, but this merely led to it being shaded out. In good years, when the exclosures have been carefully weeded and cleared of scrub, there can be dozens of plants (Whild & Lockton, 2000).

There are several other scattered sites around the county where it has been found, including Oakly Park (SO4876, Henry Spare, 1841), The Weald Moors (SJ6715, R. Anslow 1865, Longnor (SJ4800, Griffith Griffiths, 1870), Newport (SJ7419, Tavia MacLean, 1971), Crudgington Moor (SJ6517, C.W. Ward, 1974), The Walls, Chesterton (SO7896, Joan Brown, 1994) and Beck (or Beek) Moors (SJ5707, J. Rigby, 1992).

Thalictrum minus L.
Lesser Meadow-rue
Neophyte. Extinct (1841).

Edwin Lees recorded this species in the Wyre Forest at Buttonoak (SO7578) in about 1841. It seems likely to have been a garden escape.

Thelypteris palustris Schott.
Marsh Fern
Native. Rare.

This species occurs only on the peaty margins of some of the meres, and it seems to thrive in open woodland of the W5 *Alnus glutinosa-Carex paniculata* community. It has been recorded in thirteen sites, but is now reduced to just five.

It was first recorded by Edward Williams at Top Pool, Berrington (SJ5207) in about 1800, where it was later seen by William Phillips in 1878. The Reverend W.W. How found it at Whittington (SJ3231) some time before 1877, but it has not been recorded there again.

R. Anslow recorded it at both Bomere (SJ4908) and Shomere (SJ5007) pools in 1877. At Bomere it was later recorded by William Phillips (1878) and Martin Wigginton (1979). At Shomere it has been seen many times, and it is still abundant near the margin of the pool (Lockton, 2004), extending tens of metres onto the wooded Shomere Moss.

The Reverend J.H.E. Charter recorded it at Marton Pool, Baschurch (SJ4423) in 1877. It has not been seen at that site again, but it has been recorded at nearby Fenemere (SJ4422, Rose, 1959) and at The Yesters (SJ4322, Sinker, 1965), which are part of the same peatland. It persisted at Fenemere until recently (last seen by Whild & Walker in 1996).

It was also in 1877 that it was first recorded at Cole Mere (SJ4333, W.T. Burges). Diamond listed it as there in 1891, and Ian Bonner found it in 1969 by the adjacent Black Coppice Pool, where it still was in 2004 (Lockton).

In 1951 Donald Skelding found it at Oss Mere (SJ5643) and Shrawardine Pool (SJ3916). It has since been recorded at Oss Mere by Wigginton (1979), J.K. Rodwell (1982) and S.A. Ellis (1985), but not at Shrawardine Pool again.

Sinker first recorded it at Sweat Mere (SJ4330) in 1958, where it has been seen many times since. It is quite rare near the edge of the pool (Lockton, 2003). Chris

Walker found it at nearby Whattal Moss (SJ4330) in 1980.

The only other currently known site in the county is Morton Pool (SJ3023), where it was found by Chris Walker and Andrew Hearle in 1986, and was still present in some abundance in 2003 (Whild & Lockton).

Thelypteris palustris

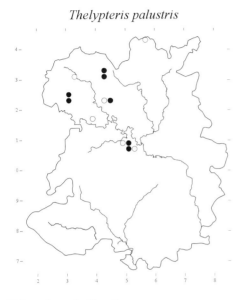

Tilia platyphyllos Scop.
Large-leaved Lime
Native. Scarce.

The native distribution of this species is difficult to ascertain because it is widely planted and sometimes misidentified. The first record for the county was in 1909, on Wenlock Edge near Longville (SO5493). Augustin Ley and William Moyle Rogers considered it to be 'probably native, or at least utterly unlikely to have been planted' there. It has not been recorded at Longville Coppice again, and was probably destroyed when the wood was converted into a conifer plantation. There are, however, a few other places on Wenlock Edge where it does still occur, as at Edge Wood (SJ6100) and Easthope Wood (SO5695) (Prestwood, 1993); Coats Wood (SO5392) and Blakeway Coppice (SO5999) (Whild & Lockton, 2003); and Wolverton Wood (SO4787, D.L. Buckingham, 2000).

At Earl's Hill (SJ4104) it is more convincingly native. It was first recorded by

Francis Rose and Charles Sinker in 1960. It occurs at the top of the cliffs on the east side of the hill, as well as by the Habberley Brook as far downstream as Lyd Hole (SJ4105, Sinker & Perring, 1966) and Radlith (SJ4105, Thorne, 2004). It was also recorded on the other side of the stream, in Oaks Wood (SJ4104) by Robert Cameron in 1978, but has not been seen there again.

Anthony Gepp found it in a hedge at Benthall Hall (SJ6502) and at the top of Benthall Edge (SJ6503) in 1941, where it has also been recorded by T.A. Hulse (1942), Stokes (1994) & Peterken (2001). In 1979 R.W. Tobin found several trees marking a parish boundary in nearby Tick Wood (SJ6403, conf. O. Rackham). Other woods where it is recorded include Kinsley Wood (SO2872, Sinker, 1968) and Nortoncamp Wood (SO4481, Henry Hand, 1977 & Rob Rowe, 1981). It is widely planted elsewhere.

Tilia platyphyllos

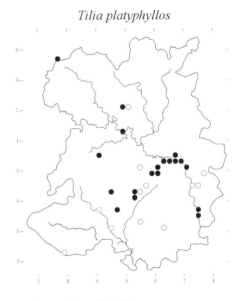

Torilis nodosa (L.) Gaertn.
Knotted Hedge-parsley
Native. Rare.

Edward Williams recorded this species at Berrington (SJ5206) and Condover (SJ4906) in about 1800. Leighton lists Ludlow (SO5175, McGhie), Much Wenlock (SO6299, Brookes) and pastures near Bomere Pool (SJ4908, Dickinson) in 1841. It grows in arable fields and waste places on base-rich soils.

Griffith Griffiths found it on road sides at Church Stretton (SO4593) in 1870. Phillips reported it still present near Bomere Pool in 1878. Beckwith found it at Kenley (SJ5600) in 1882. This, like the Much Wenlock site, is on Wenlock Edge, where it was also recorded by George Potts at Presthope (SO5897) in 1903.

Torilis nodosa

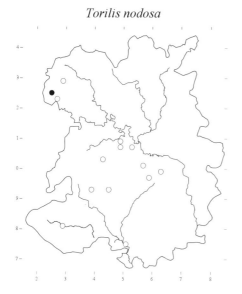

Diamond (1891) recorded it in gravelly fields near Oswestry (ca. SJ2929). Doris Pugh found it on Llanymynech Hill (SJ2622) in 1970 and 1978, although this record is claimed for Montgomeryshire by Trueman *et al.*, 1995. Ruth and Allan Dawes recorded it on Moelydd (SJ2425) in 1996.

Richard Benson recorded it on the roadside at Church Pulverbatch (SJ4202) in 1897. Trueman saw it at Clun Castle (SO2980) in 1980 and 1994. Finally, Sylvia Kingsbury had it come up in her garden in Wentnor (SO3892), presumably from buried seed, in 1993 and 1994. Owing to its temporary appearance in most sites, it is perhaps just a casual in Shropshire.

Trichophorum cespitosum (L.) Hartman
Deergrass
Native. Scarce.

There are two distinct habitats for this species in Shropshire: upland moors and lowland bogs, both characterised by peat soils. Edward Williams found Deergrass in both of these situations in about 1800, at Shawbury Heath (SJ5420) and Silvington Common (SO6279). Edward Elsmere also saw it at Shawbury Heath in about 1841, and Andrew Bloxam recorded it on Whixall Moss (SJ4936) at about the same time. Leighton collected it at Twyford Vownog (SJ3426), part of the Rednal Moss complex, on 26th June 1840. His specimens are at BM and E, and have since been shown to be of the rare northern subspecies *T. cespitosum* ssp. *cespitosum* (det. G.A. Swan) – the only record for the county, and the earliest known record of it in Britain.

In 1856 George Jorden listed it for 'Oreton, Farlow & adjacent parts,' which might have been a reference to Oreton Common, the last remnant of which is the Wildlife Trust's reserve at Cramer Gutter (SO6479). It was first recorded specifically at that site by Martin Wigginton in 1981, and has since been seen many times, most recently by Whild & Lockton in 2001. The plants there are confirmed to be of the more common subspecies *germanicum*, as is probably the case for all other populations in the county.

William Beckwith found it at Clarepool Moss (SJ4334) in 1882, but it has not been seen there since. Other lowland sites for it are Hodnet Heath (SJ6128), where it was found by Francis Rose in 1965 and has since been recorded by S.B. Chapman (1969) and Chris Walker (1981 & 1994); Steel Heath (SJ5436), where it was recorded by Ron Porley in 1983; Puleston Bog (SJ7323), where Bryan Fowler saw it in 1978 & 1986; and Wem Moss (SJ4734), where Sarah Whild found it in vehicle tracks after management operations in 1999.

It seems to occur in three separate areas in the uplands, in the south-east, south-west and north-west corners of the county. In the Titterstone Clee area it is recorded in six 1km squares, the most recent records for which are: Titterstone Clee (SO5977 & SO6078, Kate Thorne, 1999), Silvington Common (SO6278, I.C. Trueman, 1998; SO6279, J.H.S. Cox, 1991); Catherton Common (SO6478 & SO6479, E. Heywood-Waddington, 1988). In the south-west of the county it grows at Rhos Fiddle (SO2085, Hillman & Hearle, 1992; Thorne, 2000) and Lower Short Ditch (SO2288, Cox, 1991). In the north-west, there is just one record, for Selattyn Hill (SJ2534) by Marjorie Wainwright in 1982.

Trichophorum cespitosum

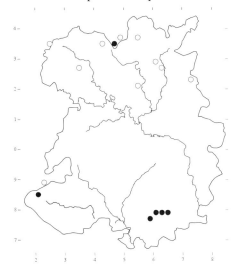

Trollius europaeus L.
Globe-flower
Native. Scarce.

Shropshire is on the edge of the range for this northerly, upland species, but in the past it was not uncommon in the north-west of the county. It was plentiful in the meadows at The Hayes, Oswestry (SJ2830) when Richard Hill Waring recorded it there in 1770, and was later seen there by Salwey in 1841 and Beckwith in 1889 (although Beckwith thought it had escaped from gardens). Edward Williams recorded it in two places near Halston Hall (SJ3331 & SJ3532) in about 1800, and Dovaston considered it to be very common at Aston (SJ3227) and Maesbury (SJ3025) in about 1841.

Trollius europaeus

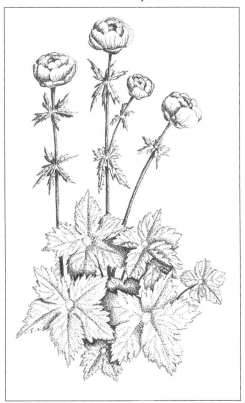

The historical sites are too numerous to list individually, but there are now just six remaining populations, each with just a few plants. The sites are: Crofts Mill (SJ3024, Will Prestwood, 1982; John Thompson & Kate Thorne, 1998), Nantmawr (SJ2524, Ruth Dawes and Pat Parker, 1993), Pentre-Dafydd (SJ2832, Rob Mileto, 2001), Porth-y-waen (SJ2523, E.R. Lloyd, 1937; Ruth Dawes, 1993), Sweeny Fen (SJ2725, Ian Bonner, 1966, and numerous recorders since), and Trefonen Marshes (SJ2426, E.D. Pugh, 1979, and numerous recorders since). At Sweeny Fen it is now very rare, and the two plants are protected from grazing by wire cages, but they are becoming overgrown by trees. At Trefonen Marshes it was reported by Ruth Dawes to be thriving in 1998.

Trollius europaeus

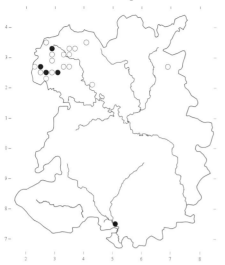

Ulmus minor Mill.
Small-leaved Elm
Archaeophyte. Rare.

This appears to be a hedgerow tree in Shropshire, and is almost certainly planted wherever it occurs. Leighton recorded '*Ulmus campestris*, Common small-leaved Elm' in hedges in 1841, but did not give any localities. Frank Perring found it in scattered places Attingham Park in 1972, and considered it 'obviously planted.'

Henry Hand recorded a tree at Henley (SO4488) in 1973, but after a 'slight attack of disease' it was felled in 1976. Winifred Hutton found one on the west side of The Walls, Chesterton (SO7896) in 1976 and another one at Woundale (SO7792) in 1979. Perring found it in Aqueduct Plantation (SJ6815) in 1977, and Sarah Stafford recorded that a tree she found at Rowton (SJ3813) in 1978 was dead by 1981. Bryan Fowler recorded a half-dead tree at Pontesbury (SJ4005) in 1980. There are no more good records of this species in the county, although tetrad records were sent in for SO79N, SO59P and SJ74F in the 1990s.

Ulmus plotii Druce
Plot's Elm
Native. Rare.

George Druce first recorded Plot's Elm at Shrewsbury (SJ4912) in 1921. In 1942 W.T.

Stern collected it at Shawbury (SJ5521) and Lee Brockhurst (SJ5426) (both det. R. Melville, K). In 1980 Bill Thompson made a tentative record for Alveley (SO7683) but that has never been confirmed. In 1994 Ruth and Allan Dawes collected a specimen of *Ulmus* ×*viminalis* (*U. minor* × *plotii*) from a hedgerow at Tan-y-graig (SJ2125, det. P.J. Bourne). There have been no other records of this supposedly endemic species, and it is now difficult to record as a result of the elm decline following the outbreak of Dutch Elm Disease in the 1970s. Many elms seem to be recovering to some extent now, however.

[Utricularia australis R.Br.]
Bladderwort
Not in Shropshire.

There is only one record so far of this species in the county. Arthur Bennett identified it from an unlabelled specimen in William Beckwith's herbarium long after he died. There is no evidence that it came from Shropshire, and Bennett's determination alone is insufficient to establish that it really was that species, so it is probably best ignored. The 1842 record in Sinker's Flora for Seaman's Moss Pits probably relates to a site in Cheshire.

Utricularia minor L.
Lesser Bladderwort
Native. Rare.

This species is typical of peat cuttings in lowland raised bogs, and in Shropshire it may have occurred on many of the mosses at some point in the past. Williams recorded it at Shomere Pool (SJ5007), Knockin Heath (SJ3521), and Rednal Moss (SJ3427) in about 1800. In 1805 Aikin found it at Whixall Moss (SJ4936). Babington & Leighton collected it at Bomere Pool (SJ4908) in 1835, and Bowman & Bloxam also saw it at Whixall Moss in 1841.

William Phillips revisited Leighton's site at Bomere Pool in 1878; and Beckwith also saw it there in 1880. In Diamond's Flora of Oswestry (1891) it is listed for Clarepool Moss (SJ4334), where it was probably found by O.M. Feilden.

In Hamilton's lost Flora of 1913 there were records for the vicinity of Crose Mere (SJ4300) and Cole Mere (SJ4333), but the details are lost.

Gilbert Johnson recorded it at Whixall Moss again in 1910, and it has since been seen there by Wilson (1950), Sinker (1962), Hearle (1988), Perring (1989), Parker (1994) and Boardman (2004). It is just one small patch in an old peat cutting, but it has apparently been thriving in recent years.

Utricularia minor

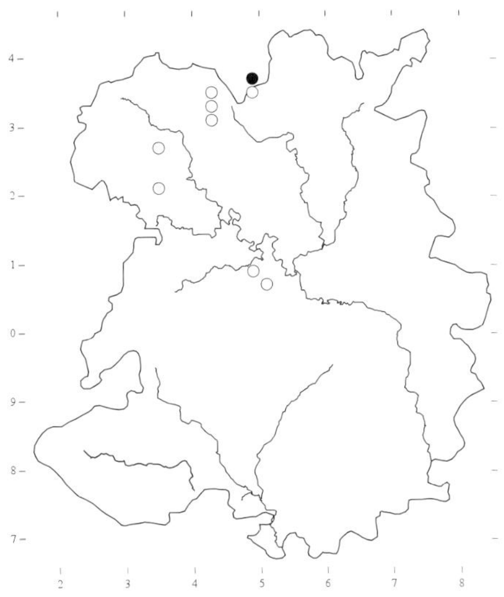

Utricularia vulgaris L.
Greater Bladderwort
Native. Extinct (1903).

Apart from the one specimen that has been properly determined, the account below refers to the *U. vulgaris* aggregate, and it might well turn out to include *U. australis* and possibly other taxa.

Greater Bladderwort occurs throughout the British Isles, and is not at all rare, but in the Midlands it has declined almost to extinction. It occurs in more base-rich waters than Lesser Bladderwort. Its best known site in Shropshire was Hencott Pool (SJ4916), where it was first recorded by Edward Williams in about 1800, and was later seen by Francis Dickinson (1841), William Beckwith (1882) and finally by William Hamilton (1901 & 1903). Williams also recorded it in a pool at Eaton Mascott

(SJ5305), in ditches at Halston (SJ3431), and in pits at Battlefield (SJ5117). At about the same time, Arthur Aikin found it in a small pond on Sharpstones Hill (SJ4909).

John Bowman recorded it in a ditch on the north side of Crose Mere (SJ4230) in 1836. Dovaston collected it at Rednal Moss (SJ3426) in 1841 (conf. C.D. Preston, SHY), and curiously described it as 'naturalised' there. Leighton recorded it at nearby Twyford Vownog (SJ3426).

In 1865 R. Anslow recorded it on the Weald Moors (ca. SJ6717) and in 1878 Phillips found it still at Battlefield. He later found it at Newton Bog (SJ4816) and Kynnersley (SJ6517).

In addition to refinding it at Hencott Pool, Beckwith found it at Clarepool Moss (SJ4334), Kynnersley Moor (SJ6716) and Fenemere (SJ4422) in the early 1880s. Diamond listed it for Lyneal Moss (SJ4434) and Frankton (SJ3632) in 1891. There are a few other sites apparently listed in Hamilton's missing Flora of 1913, but the details are unknown. Unless any of these supersede Hamilton's own record of 1903, that is the last time it was recorded in the county.

Utricularia vulgaris s.l.

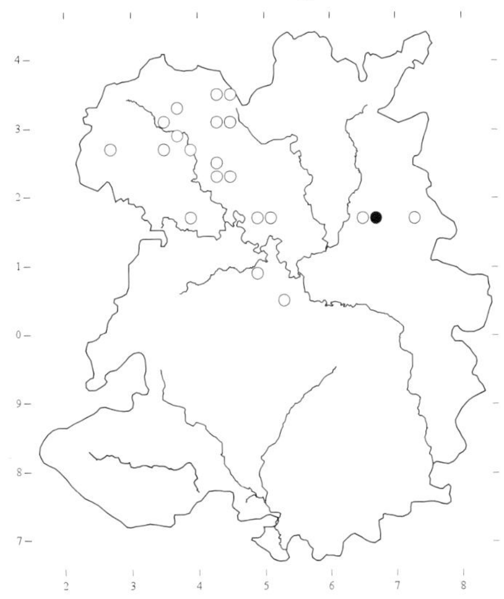

Vaccinium ^xintermedium Ruthe
(Vaccinium myrtillus × *vitis-idaea)*
Hybrid Bilberry
Native. Rare.

Charles Sinker spotted this hybrid on the Stiperstones ridge near Manstone Rock (SO3698) in 1968. It was not recorded again until 2002, when Kate Thorne found it near Cranberry Rock (SO3698), Blakemoorgate (SJ3801) and Nipstone Rock (SO3596) (conf. K.V. Cavalot).

Vaccinium vitis-idaea L.
Cowberry
Native. Scarce.

Littleton Brown first recorded this species on the Stiperstones in about 1725. Since then it has been recorded many times, and it is still frequent from Black Rhadley (SO3495, Kingsbury & Lockton, 1996) northwards to Castle Ring (SJ3701) and Blakemoorgate (SJ3801) (Whild & Lockton, 1995), occurring in a total of 12 1km squares.

Vaccinium vitis-idaea

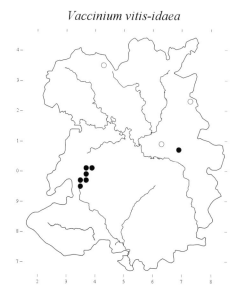

Elsewhere in the county it is known only on an old pit mound in Telford Town Park (SJ6907), where it was discovered by Jeff Davies in 1980 and was last recorded by John Box in 1995. Bryan Fowler's record for Puleston Common (SJ7323, 1978) has not been repeated, and neither has R.M.

Serjeantson's 1882 record for 'The Longmynds,' although that could be a reference to the Stiperstones. The details of two other old records given by Sinker (SJ43H & SJ60J, ca. 1913) are not known.

Valerianella dentata (L.) Pollich
Narrow-fruited Cornsalad
Archaeophyte. Rare.

Although this was once a widespread agricultural weed it is now very rare in the county. Kate Thorne found it on the edge of a field of beet near Hinton (SJ4008) in 1991 (conf. I.C. Trueman) but it was not there again in subsequent years; and Dave Buckingham recorded it (with no specimen) on the edge of a quarry on Wenlock Edge (SO5898) in 2000. Otherwise, there have been no records for nearly 100 years.

Valerianella eriocarpa Desv.
Hairy-fruited Cornsalad
Archaeophyte. Extinct (1922).

It is now widely accepted that this species is an introduction in Britain, and it only seems to occur here as a rare casual. In Shropshire it was collected by Leighton near Sharpstones Hill (SJ4909) in 1837; W.B. Allen claimed to have found it at Benthall (SJ6602) in 1904; and J.C. Melvill collected it at Meole Brace (SJ4810) in 1922.

Verbascum lychnitis L.
White Mullein
Neophyte. Rare.

Henry Spare, who was a somewhat unreliable botanist, recorded this species at Downton Hall (SO5279) in about 1841; Beckwith & Serjeantson found it near Snow Pool (SJ5706) in 1880; and Dr & Mrs Sturt recorded it as a garden escape at Aston Munslow (SO5186) in 1997. There seems little reason to consider it a native species in the county.

Vicia lathyroides L.
Spring Vetch
Native. Rare.

This species occurs in short, acid grassland of the community U1 *Festuca ovina-Agrostis capillaris-Rumex acetosella* grassland, which is quite widespread in Shropshire and is sometimes very species-rich. It was first recorded in the county by Henry Spare at Whitcliffe (SO4974) in 1841. In 1960 Hildred Bigwood found it at Ryton (S7602). Bryan Fowler discovered it at Rudge (SO8097) in 1978, and it was still there in 1996 (R.M. Stokes). Moira Williams recorded it in an old quarry on Clunbury Hill (SO3779) in 1980 and Jean Hooson found it on Prees Higher Heath (SJ5735) in 1994 (conf. C. Walker).

Vicia lathyroides

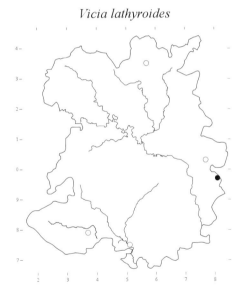

Viola canina L.
Heath Dog-violet
Native. Scarce.

Leighton (1841) did not distinguish *Viola canina* from *V. riviniana*, and most of the records he gives are clearly for the latter, but his record for Twyford Vownog (=Rednal Moss, SJ3426) could well have been of Heath Dog-violet, as this species is more likely to be found on heaths and mires.

The next record was not until 1976, when Malcolm Clark reported it at Sturt Common

(SO7277). John Bingham has since recorded it in two other places in the Wyre Forest, at SO77N and SO77P (both in 1997). Sinker's (1985) assertion that it occurs in several places in the Wyre Forest does not seem to be supported by any records.

Paul Bell found it on Betton Moss (SJ6836) in 1977, and later saw it there in 1986 and 1987. Mary Fuller recorded it at Speller Coppice (SO5089) in 1977, but it had gone by 1986. Martin Wigginton and Chris Walker recorded it at Stocking Meadows (SO6580) in 1981; and Dan Wrench found it at Gulley Green (SJ3101) and Horseditch (SO5977) in 1994 (where Guy Stone & Rob Mileto later saw it in 1996). Also in 1994 Pat Parker and Ruth Dawes recorded it at Chetwynd Heath (SJ7122).

In 1997 John Bingham made records of it at Cornbrook (SO6075) and Brown Clee (SO5886).

None of the above records is supported by a voucher specimen, and there are few instances of it being reliably recorded more than once in any site, so it would be useful to have proof that this species does really occur in the county.

Viola canina

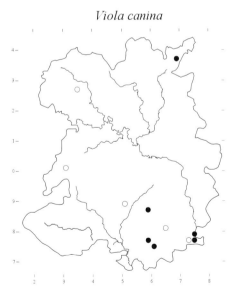

Wahlenbergia hederacea (L.) Rchb.
Ivy-leaved Bellflower
Native. Scarce.

This species has an unusual distribution, being largely confined to the warm oceanic regions of the south-west. It is therefore close to its north-easterly limit in Shropshire, although there are a few isolated populations on hills further north.

The only place in the county where it has been recorded more than once is Titterstone Clee, where it was first recorded by Edward Williams in about 1800, on the 'north side, towards the bottom' (SO5978). It has since been recorded many times, on all sides of the hill, and is currently known in ten 1km squares there.

Elsewhere in the county it has been recorded at Caer Caradoc (SO4795, G.M. Furley, 1922), Cothercott Hill (SJ4100, B. Fowler, 1980), at Diddlebury Common (SO4886, G.

Potts, 1922) and in Clun Forest (SO2286, Thorne, 2002).

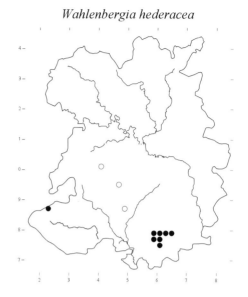

Wahlenbergia hederacea

Key to Herbaria

Following codes given by Kent & Allen, 1984.

ABD	Department of Botany, University of Aberdeen
ABRN	Monks Wood Experimental Station
BIRM	University of Birmingham
BM	Natural History museum
CGE	University of Cambridge Botany School
CLE	Carlisle Museum & Art Gallery
DBN	National Botanic Gardens, Glasnevin
E	Royal Botanic Garden, Edinburgh
GL	University of Glasgow
GW	West of Scotland College of Agriculture
HLU	University of Hull
HWB	Butler Museum, Harrow School
K	Royal Botanic Gardens, Kew
LDL	Ludlow Museum
LINN	Linnean Society of London
LIV	Liverpool Museum
LIVU	University of Liverpool
LTR	University of Leicester
MANCH	Manchester Museum
NMW	National Museum of Wales
OXF	University of Oxford
RNG	University of Reading
SHY	Shrewsbury Museum
SHYB	Shrewsbury School
SLBI	South London Botanical Institute
SUN	Sunderland Museum
TCD	Trinity College, Dublin
WARMS	Warwickshire Museum

References

Aikin, A. 1797. *Journal of a tour through North Wales and part of Shropshire; with observations in mineralogy, and other branches of natural history.* London.

Babington, A. 1897. *Memorials, Journal and Botanical Correspondence of Charles Cardale Babington.* Macmillan & Bowes, Cambridge.

Beckwith, W.E. 1881, 1882 & 1901. Notes on Shropshire Plants. *Journal of Botany* 19: 48-51, 106-111, 143-149; 20: 342-346, 363-368; 39: 182-186.

Benson, R. de G. 1904. 'Phanerogams.' In Campbell-Hyslop, C.W. & Cobbold, E.S. *Church Stretton, some results of Local Scientific Research,* vol. 2, 62-135. Wilding, Shrewsbury.

Briggs, J.D. 1988. *Montgomery Canal Ecological Survey Survey Report 1985-1888.* British Waterways, Llanymynech (unpublished).

Britton, C.E. 1918. *Report for 1917.* The Botanical Society & Exchange Club of the British Isles. T. Buncle & Co., Arbroath.

Burnham, C.P. & Mackney, D. 1964. Soils of Shropshire. *Field Studies* 2 (1) 83-107.

Butcher, R.W. & Strudwick, F.E. 1930. *Further Illustrations of British Plants.* L. Reeve & Co., Kent.

Caradoc & Severn Valley Field Club. 1891-1970. *Record of Bare Facts.* Shrewsbury.

Carter, P.W. 1960. The Botanical Exploration of Shropshire. *Transactions of the Caradoc & Severn Valley Field Club* 1951-1956.

Clarke, W.A. 1900. *First British Records of Flowering Plants.* West, Newman & Co., London.

Cox, J.H.S. & Aitchison, J.W. 1994. *Biological Survey of Common Land No 24: Shropshire.* Rural Surveys Research Unit, University of Wales, Aberystwyth.

Cox, T.A. 1855. Discovery of *Nuphar lutea* in Shropshire. *The Phytologist New Series* 1, 127.

Desmond, R. 1994. *Dictionary of British & Irish Botanists and Horticulturists.* Taylor & Francis, London.

Diamond, T. 1891. *A Flora of Oswestry and the District.* Oswestry.

Farrell, L. & Perring, F.H. 1996. Guidelines for the Preparation of County Rare Plant Registers. *BSBI News* 71, 10-11.

Garner, R. 1844. *The Natural History of the County of Stafford; comprising its Geology, Zoology, Botany, and Meteorology, &c.* Van Voorst, London.

Griffiths, G.H. 1871. On the more rare plants of the Longmynds. *Transactions of the Woolhope Naturalists' Field Club 1870,* 148-157.

Griffiths, G.H. n.d. (c.1870) *A Botanical Guide to the environs to Church Stretton: comprising a classified arrangement of the indigenous flowers and ferns.* J.O. Sandford, Shrewsbury.

Hamilton, W.P. (ed) Botany. In Page, W. 1908. *The Victoria History of Shropshire* pp 51-100. The Victoria History of the Counties of England. Constable, London.

Hamilton, W.P. 1913. *Flora of Shropshire.* Unpublished manuscript formerly in the possession of Shrewsbury Library.

Haslam, S., Sinker, C. & Wolseley, P. 1975. British Water Plants. *Field Studies* 4 (2), 243-351.

Hill, M.O., Mountford, J.O., Roy, D.B., & Bunce, R.G.H. 1999. *Ellenberg's indicator values for British plants.* Institute of Terrestrial Ecology, Huntingdon.

Houghton, W. 1870. The Weal Moors. *Caradoc & Severn Valley Field Club Papers 1865-1870,* 103-112.

Johnson, G. 1911. Birds and Flowers of Shelton Rough. *Transactions of the Caradoc & Severn Valley Field Club* 5 (2).

Jorden, G. 1856. Some account of the botany of the Wyre Forest and surrounding parts of the Country. *The Phytologist New Series* 1, 281-286 & 354-361.

Kay, Q.O.N., John. R.F. & Jones, R.A. 1999. Biology, genetic variation and conservation of *Luronium natans* (L.) Raf. in Britain and Ireland. *Watsonia* 22: 301-315.

Kent, D.H. & Allen, D.E. 1984. *British and Irish Herbaria*. Botanical Society of the British Isles, London.

Leighton, W.A. 1836. *A Guide through the Town of Shrewsbury*. John Davies, Shrewsbury.

Leighton, W.A. 1841. *A Flora of Shropshire*. John van Voorst, London & John Davies, Shrewsbury.

Lloyd, L.C. & Rutter, E.M. 1957. *Handlist of the Shropshire Flora*. Caradoc & Severn Valley Field Club, Shrewsbury.

Lockton, A., Whild, S. & Pearman, D. 2001. Guidelines for County Rare Plant Registers. BSBI, Shrewsbury.

Lockton, A., Whild, S., Trueman, I., Walker, C. & Parker, P. 1995. *Rare Plants of Shropshire*. Shrewsbury Museums Service, Shrewsbury.

Lockton, A.J. & Whild, S.J. 1995. *Rare Plants of Shropshire* 2nd edition. Shropshire Flora Group, Shrewsbury.

Mallabar, J. 1998. *Habitat status and niche requirements of* Carex elongata *L. in Britain*. MSc dissertation, School of Biological Sciences, University of Birmingham.

Oswald, P.H. 1985. History of botanical recording. In Sinker *et al.*, 1985, 11-40.

Oswald, P.H. 1995. History of botanical recording in Montgomeryshire. In Trueman, Morton & Wainwright, 1995, 1-24.

Perring, F H & Walters, S M. 1962. *Atlas of the British Flora*. Botanical Society of the British Isles, London.

Perring, F.H. & Farrell, L. 1977. *British Red Data Books: 1. Vascular Plants*. Society for the Promotion of Nature Conservation, Lincoln.

Perring, F.H. 1975. *Flora of Attingham*. Unpublished.

Phillips, W. 1877/78. The Filices, Lycopodiaceae, Marsiliaceae, and Equisetaceae of Shropshire. *Transactions of the Shropshire Archaeological and Natural History Society* 1: 153-158.

Phillips, W. 1878. *A Guide to the Botany, Ornithology and Geology of Shrewsbury and its Vicinity*. Shrewsbury.

Plymley, J. 1803. *A General View of the Agriculture of Shropshire*. London.

Preston, C.D. 1995. *Pondweeds of Great Britain and Ireland*. Botanical Society of the British Isles, London.

Preston, C.D., Pearman, D.A. & Dines, T.D. 2002. *New Atlas of the Flora of Britain & Ireland*. Oxford University Press, Oxford.

Preston, C.D., Pearman, D.A. & Hall, A.R. 2004. Archaeophytes in Britain. *Botanical Journal of the Linnean Society* 145, 257-294.

Ratcliffe, D. (ed.). 1977. *A Nature Conservation Review*. Cambridge University Press, Cambridge.

Rodwell, J.S. (ed) 1991-2000. *British Plant Communities* Vols 1-5. Cambridge University Press, Cambridge.

Rose, F. & Bellamy, D.J. 1959. *Botanical report on the lakes, schwingmoors and raised bogs of the north-west Midlands*. Nature Conservancy, Attingham (unpublished).

Salwey, T. 1855. Botany of the Parish, in Cathrall, W. *The History of Oswestry*, George Lewis, Oswestry.

Sinker, C.A. 1962. *The North Shropshire Meres and Mosses - a background for ecologists*. Field Studies Vol. 1 No. 4. Reprinted Headley Brothers Ltd., London.

Sinker, C.A., Packham, J.R., Trueman, I.C., Oswald, P.H., Perring, F.H. & Prestwood, W.V. 1985. *Ecological Flora of the Shropshire Region*. Shropshire Trust for Nature Conservation, Shrewsbury.

Stace, C.A. 1997. *New Flora of the British Isles*, 2nd edition. Cambridge University Press.

Stewart, A., Pearman, D.A., & Preston, C.D. 1994. *Scarce Plants in Britain*. JNCC, Peterborough.

Swan, G.A. 1999. Identification, distribution and a new nothosubspecies of *Trichophorum cespitosum* (L.) Hartman (Cyperaceae) in the British Isles and N.W. Europe. *Watsonia* 22:209-233.

Trueman, I C, Morton, A & Wainwright, M. 1995. *The Flora of Montgomeryshire*. Montgomery Field Society & Montgomeryshire Wildlife Trust, Welshpool.

Turner, D. & Dillwyn, L.W. 1805. *Botanist's Guide through England & Wales*. Phillips & Fardon, London.

Watson, H.C. 1835. *The New Botanist's Guide to the localities of the rarer plants of Britain*, vol. 1: England & Wales. Longman, Rees, Orme, Brown, Green & Longman, London.

Whild, S.J. & Lockton, A.J. 2003. *Carex muricata* subsp. *muricata* (Cyperaceae) in Shropshire. *Watsonia* 24: 528-531.

Whild, S.J. & Lockton, A.J. 2004. Species of Conservation Significance. *Shropshire Botanical Society Newsletter* 10:12-15.

Wigginton, M.J. 1980. *Survey of the Shropshire, Cheshire & Staffordshire Meres*. England Field Unit Report No. 1. Nature Conservancy Council, Banbury.

Wigginton, M.J. 1989. *Survey of Shropshire and Cheshire Meres*. England Field Unit Report No. 59. Nature Conservancy Council, Banbury.

Wigginton, M.J. 1999. *British Red Data Books 1: Vascular plants* (3rd edition). Joint Nature Conservation Committee, Peterborough.